Grade 4

Practice Book B

B

The McGraw·Hill Companies

Published by Macmillan/McGraw-Hill, of McGraw-Hill Education, a division of The McGraw-Hill Companies, Inc., Two Penn Plaza, New York, New York 10121.

Printed in the United States of America

4 5 6 7 8 9 10 066 09 08 07

Contents

Unit 1 • Let's Explore

Unit 2 • Take a Stand

Unit 3 • Making a Difference

Unit 4 • Viewpoints

Unit 5 • Relationships

Unit 6 • Discovery

Name ______________________________

allergies	assignments	suspicious	accuse
consideration	consume	evidence	

Pair vocabulary words and write a sentence for each pair. For example:

He did not want to *accuse* John until he had *evidence* against him.

Underline each vocabulary word in the sentences you write. You will need to use one word twice.

1. ______________________________

2. ______________________________

3. ______________________________

4. ______________________________

Name ______________________________

You are going to write a story that has a main character who solves a mystery. Circle your choices below, or choose names, character quality, and a problem of your own. Then write a story using the items you circled. Be sure to give a clear description of the problem and how the character solves it.

Main Character's Name:

Roberto Heather McKenzie Jake Allison Andre

Important Fact about Character:

curious artistic good athlete friendly works alone

Mystery:

at school at home with friends
something found connected to a sport or activity something lost

____

____

____

____

____

____

____

____

____

____

____

____

At Home: Have the student find a story in the newspaper or a magazine about someone who solves a problem. Identify the problem and solution.

Name ______________________________

As you read *The Mystery of the Missing Lunch,* fill in the Problem and Solution Chart.

Problem

↓

Action

↓

Action

↓

Action

↓

Solution

How does the information you wrote in the Problem and Solution Chart help you to analyze *The Mystery of the Missing Lunch*?

At Home: Have the student use the chart to retell the story.

Name ______________________________

As I read, I will pay attention to end punctuation in each sentence.

Vera and Mario were walking home from school. As
9 they followed their usual path through the park, they enjoyed
19 watching everything that went on. Squirrels raced up and
28 down the trees. Ducks swam across the pond and quacked
38 loudly. Neighbors walked their dogs across the grass.
46 Children swung on the swings and played ball in the field.
57 This day's walk began like any other for Vera and Mario,
68 but that soon changed. Vera stopped suddenly and pointed.
77 "Look at that!" she said with surprise.
84 Mario looked straight ahead. A large amount of trash was
94 on the ground near the pond. It was an ugly sight. The kids
107 walked closer to see exactly what was there. They saw plastic
118 bags, dirty paper plates and cups, and empty juice cartons.
128 There were chicken bones, half-eaten ears of corn, and
137 watermelon skins. Some of the trash was right at the edge of
149 the pond. 151

Comprehension Check

1. What problem do Vera and Mario discover? **Problem and Solution**

2. How does the first paragraph relate to their discovery? **Problem and Solution**

	Words Read	–	Number of Errors	=	Words Correct Score
First Read		–		=	
Second Read		–		=	

At Home: Help the student read the passage, paying attention to the goal at the top of the page.

Name ___________________________

Charts are a good way to show information. There are **rows** that go across a chart. There are **columns** that go up and down in a chart.

Make a chart using the following data:

Write a title for a chart about Mystery Books.

Write in the names of three mystery books you might write.

Write the prices you might charge for your books.

Write how many copies you might sell.

When you finish your chart, write two or more sentences about how the chart might help someone looking for a book.

At Home: Have the student make a chart of three or four favorite books that he or she has read. List the title, the main character, what the story is about, and the number of pages.

Name ______________________________

Choose a word you do not already know, and create a dictionary entry for it. When you are finished, create another entry with a different word.

At Home: Together, make up words and assign definitions to them.

Name ____________________

Choose a consonant. Then write as many words with a short-vowel sound between the two consonants. For example, if you choose *n* and *p,* you might write *nip* and *nap.*

Beginning consonants: b, c, d, g, h, j, l, m, n, p, r, t, v, w

Ending consonants: b, ck, d, ff, g, ng, ll, m, n, p, r, s, t, w, y

1. Consonant pairs: ____________________

____

____

2. Consonant pairs: ____________________

____

____

3. Consonant pairs: ____________________

____

____

4. Consonant pairs: ____________________

____

____

Now write a sentence that uses three of your short-vowel words.

5. ____________________

____

At Home: Play a game: Take turns saying two consonants, such as *m* and *p*. Then put a vowel between them and say the word.

Name ______________________________

climate	silken	lumbering	swallows
lurk	shimmer	eerie	

Make your own crossword puzzle using the vocabulary words above. Give each word its own number. Then write out clues for your *across* and *down* words. Exchange puzzles with a partner.

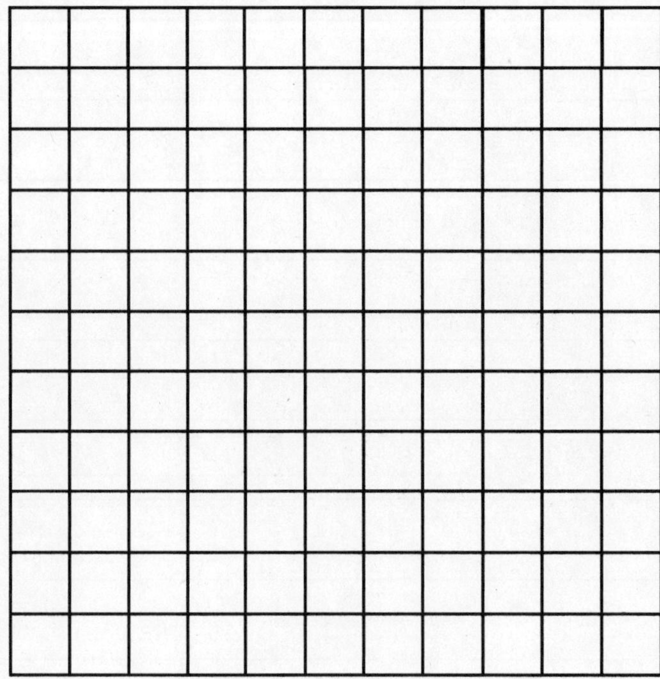

Across

____

____

____

____

Down

____

____

____

____

Name ______________________________

In the space below, write the main idea of *A Walk in the Desert.* Then think about the details and facts that support the main idea. Write about three details that most impressed you in the selection.

Main Idea: ______________________________

____

Details and Facts: ______________________________

____

____

Think about one of the animals described in *A Walk in the Desert.* How would you describe the animal to a friend or family member? Write the details below.

Animal: ______________________________

____

____

____

____

____

____

____

____

____

____

At Home: Have the student read three brief newspaper articles. For each ask the student to identify the main idea and at least two supporting details.

Name ______________________________

As you read *A Walk in the Desert*, fill in the Main Idea Chart.

Main Ideas	Details

How does the information you wrote in the Main Idea Chart help you to summarize *A Walk in the Desert*?

At Home: Have the student use the chart to retell the story.

Name ____________________

As I read, I will pay attention to tempo.

Welcome to the Great Basin Desert. It's one of four
10 deserts in North America. The Great Basin Desert is the
20 coldest of the four North American deserts.
27 The Great Basin is an area in the western United States
38 that lies between the Sierra Nevada Mountains and the Rocky
48 Mountains. The land is like a big bowl that spreads across
59 several states. The Sierra Nevada and Rocky Mountains
67 are the high places that make the edges of the bowl.
78 Rain or snow that falls in the Great Basin remains
88 there. The water evaporates or drains into the dry ground.
98 Like all deserts, the Great Basin Desert gets less than
108 10 inches (25 cm) of rain or snow each year.
116 The Great Basin Desert covers most of Nevada and
125 Utah, as well as parts of nearby states. There are many
136 smaller mountain ranges between the Sierra Nevada
143 Mountains and the Rocky Mountains. There are valleys
151 between these mountain ranges. Geologists call this
158 landscape a basin-and-range pattern. 162

Comprehension Check

1. What is the main idea of the second paragraph? **Main Idea and Details**

2. What is the main idea of the fourth paragraph? **Main Idea and Details**

	Words Read	–	Number of Errors	=	Words Correct Score
First Read		–		=	
Second Read		–		=	

At Home: Help the student read the passage, paying attention to the goal at the top of the page.

Name ______________________________

Assonance is the repetition of the same or similar vowel sounds in two or more words. **Metaphor** is a figure of speech in which two very different objects or ideas are made to seem the same. Both of these are often used in poetry.

Choose three words from the box that have assonance. Use them in a short paragraph or poem.

night	can	dip	freeze
hat	sleet	slide	pick
shine	trim	scream	rack

____

____

____

____

____

Complete each sentence with a metaphor.

1. The gila monster ______________________________
2. People in the street below ______________________________
3. Tall oak trees ______________________________
4. The mouse ______________________________
5. My grandmother ______________________________

At Home: Ask the student to read his or her poem or paragraph and to point out where it uses assonance.

Name ______________________________

An **example** is one kind of context clue. Examples can help you to figure out the meaning of an unfamiliar word.

All the words below can be used in a desert or outdoors setting. Use at least five of the words to write sentences with a desert setting. Use context clues in your writing, giving examples to help to make the meaning of each word clear.

rippled	cactus	drenched	minerals
scaly	spines	stinger	crevice
oasis	snug	landscape	terrain

1. ______________________________

____

2. ______________________________

____

3. ______________________________

____

4. ______________________________

____

5. ______________________________

____

6. ______________________________

____

At Home: Have the student explain the context clues in the sentences he or she wrote.

Name ______________________________

escape	state	take	caves	rain
waves	waiting	snakes	lakes	Maine
claim	whale	plains	play	days

Complete the story by filling in the blanks with words that have the long *a* sound. You may use some words more than once.

The Best Place

Some people **_ai__** ________________ that an eastern **__a_e** ________________, like **_ai__** ________________, is more beautiful than a desert **__a_e** ________________, like Arizona. Visitors to **_ai__** ________________ can go **__a_e** ________________ watching or catch fish in the many **__a_es** ________________. They can explore the rocky coast and **__ay** ________________ in the **__a_es** ________________ along the shore. The only problem with living in **_ai__** ________________ is **_ai_ing** ________________ until the cold **__ays** ________________ of winter are gone.

On the other hand, people who visit the desert hardly ever see snow or **_ai_** ________________. The temperature is often very hot, and people **__a_e** ________________ indoors to air conditioning when they can. Some people don't mind the heat. They like to explore **_a_es** ________________ and go hiking on the **__ai_s** ________________. They watch out for **__a_es** ________________ and **_a_e** ________________ plenty of water with them.

At Home: Have the student write a paragraph using ten words with the long *a* sound that are not on this list.

Name ________________________________

Read the vocabulary words and the sentences that follow. On the lines below rewrite each sentence, using a vocabulary word, changing the sentence's meaning.

journey	wildlife	natural	roamed	completed

1. We followed the directions and went directly to the restaurant.

____

____

2. My family has had a few dogs and cats for pets.

____

____

3. There were many artificial ingredients in the yogurt.

____

____

4. My class went on an outing this afternoon to see an exhibit at the museum.

____

____

5. Over the weekend I started reading the first book in that series.

____

____

Name ______________________________

Read each paragraph. Then answer the questions that follow.

Grand Canyon National Park invites fourth through sixth graders to participate in our education program. The program will be offered Monday through Friday between September 20 and December 10, and again between March 7 and May 27.

1. What is the main idea of this paragraph?

____

2. List the supporting details below.

____

____

3. What will the next paragraph probably be about?

____

Grand Canyon National Park is one of 270 national parks in the Vital Signs Monitoring network. Vital Signs Monitoring keeps track of each and every component of a national park as an ecosystem. It also contributes information needed to understand and measure performance regarding water quality, landscape changes, and wildlife populations.

4. What is the main idea of this paragraph?

____

5. List the supporting details below.

____

____

6. What will the next paragraph probably be about?

____

At Home: Read a medium-length newspaper article aloud to the student. Have him or her identify the article's main idea and at least three supporting details.

Name ______________________________

As you read *Animals Come Home to Our National Parks*, fill in the Main Idea Chart.

Main Ideas	Details

How does the information you wrote in the Main Idea Chart help you to summarize *Animals Come Home to Our National Parks*?

At Home: Have the student use the chart to retell the story.

Name ____________________

As I read, I will pay attention to the pronunciation of vocabulary words and other difficult words.

It was the late 1920s. Ernst Coe had moved to Florida. He began
12 to notice that plants and birds were disappearing from one of his
24 favorite places, the Everglades. The Everglades was a giant marsh full
35 of unique plants and animals that couldn't be found anywhere else.
46 Thousands of beautiful birds made the Everglades their home.
55 Turtles, manatees, and alligators roamed its waters. Ernst Coe
64 thought the Everglades should be turned into a national park.
74 Some people thought Ernst Coe was foolish. The Everglades were
84 just a swamp. In some places, all you could see was water and grass.
98 Weren't national parks supposed to be places that had spectacular
108 scenery? Luckily, new thinking about what makes a good national
118 park was taking shape in Washington, D.C. People didn't want to
129 preserve only beautiful mountains. They were hoping to protect
138 places that were unique. They wanted parks that would preserve our
149 nation's history and culture. 153

Comprehension Check

1. What problem did Ernst Coe identify and how did he want to solve it? **Problem and Solution**

2. What is the main idea in the third paragraph? **Main Idea and Details**

	Words Read	–	Number of Errors	=	Words Correct Score
First Read		–		=	
Second Read		–		=	

At Home: Help the student read the passage, paying attention to the goal at the top of the page.

Name ______________________________

park[1] pärk *noun* [Middle English, from Old French *parc* enclosure] **1** enclosed land with wildlife owned by royalty. **2 a:** land in or near a city or town used for recreation. **b:** land in its natural state owned by the public. **3** a stadium and surrounding facilities.
park[2] *verb* **1** to leave a vehicle at the edge of a street. **2** to set and leave temporarily. He *parked* himself on a chair.

Above are two sample dictionary entries for the word park. **Using these as a model, create a dictionary entry for any multiple-meaning word you choose. Be sure to include the word's correct spelling, pronunciation, part of speech, origin, and meanings.**

____

____

____

____

____

____

____

____

____

____

____

At Home: Together, look up word origins in a dictionary. Discuss how the words and meanings have changed over time.

Name ____________________

Use five of the following compound words to write a letter home to your family about a camping trip. You may create other compound words to complete your letter.

snowmobile	firefighter	crosscurrent	downpour
Yellowstone	frostbite	campfire	sagebrush
freshwater	airplane	arrowhead	grassland
backpacks	loudspeaker	thunderhead	wildlife

At Home: Together, invent compound words that describe objects in and around your home.

Name ______________________

Write a story about two friends on a hike through a national park. Include at least ten words with the long e sound formed by the letters ee, ie, and ea. Underline these words in your story.

At Home: Have the student brainstorm at least six examples of words that use each of the following long *e* spellings: *ee, ie, ea.*

Name ______________________________

endless	universe	protested	realistic
sensible	astronaut	paralyzed	

Suppose that an astronaut has returned from a trip to space. He is coming to tell the students at your school about his trip. On the lines below, write a speech for him. Include all the vocabulary words above.

Name ______________________________

Think about Gloria and the astronaut, Dr. Grace Street, in the story "The Astronaut and the Onion." Gloria is an outgoing character. Think of how the story would change if Gloria were shy instead. Some events of the story might not happen. What other events might happen instead?

List your changes on the chart below.

Story Event	The Astronaut and the Onion	The Shy Gloria
Gloria goes to the store.	She goes by herself.	
Dr. Street goes to the store.	She is buying cereal.	
Gloria gets Dr. Street's attention.	She loses control of the onion.	
Gloria and the astronaut talk.	They first talk about the astronaut's earrings.	

At Home: Have the student write a short story set in your neighborhood. Ask him or her to tell how the character's actions affect what happens in the story.

Name ______________________________

As you read *The Astronaut and the Onion,* fill in the Character Web.

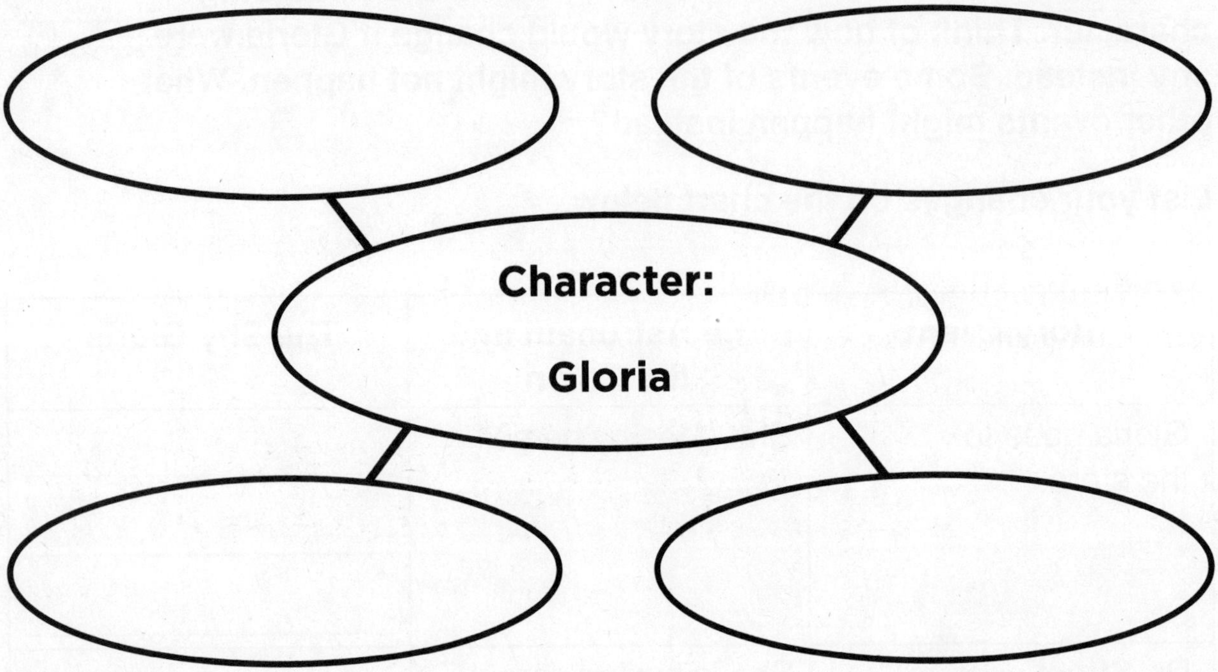

Character:

Gloria

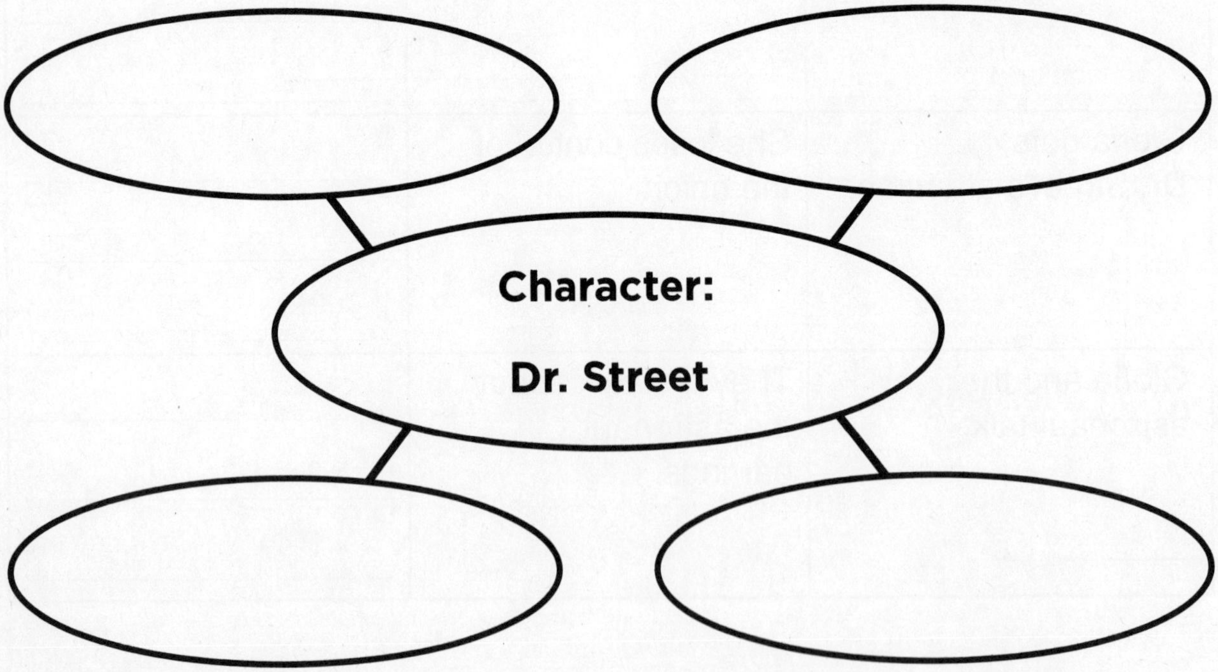

Character:

Dr. Street

How does the information you wrote in the Character Web help you analyze and make inferences about *The Astronaut and the Onion*?

At Home: Have the student use the chart to retell the story.

Name ____________________________________

As I read, I will pay attention to pauses, stops, intonation, and characters' words.

"Ready, Rae?" Commander Assad asked me. It was time to get into
12 my sleeping capsule. After a long mission in outer space, we were
24 heading home to Claryville. Everyone had to be asleep for the landing
36 on Earth. The computer would land the spaceship while we slept.
47 I climbed into my sleeping capsule and Commander Assad closed
57 the top. Pilot Velez was already asleep. The computer would close
68 Commander Assad's capsule. I shut my eyes, relaxed, and waited for
79 sleep to come. I was happy to be going home. We had been in space for
95 only a few weeks, but it had seemed **endless** at times. I missed my
109 family and friends. I couldn't wait to see everyone at school and tell
122 them about my trip.
126 Let me introduce myself. I'm Rae Chen, **astronaut**-in-training. I'm
135 the junior member of the Lotus Space Mission — that's Commander
145 Assad, Pilot Velez, and me. 150

Comprehension Check

1. Even though Rae is excited to be going home, how do you know she enjoyed her time in space? **Character**

2. What clues tell you that Rae is not a typical astronaut? **Character**

	Words Read	–	Number of Errors	=	Words Correct Score
First Read		–		=	
Second Read		–		=	

At Home: Help the student read the passage, paying attention to the goal at the top of the page.

Name ________________________________

Make a diagram that shows how far it is from either your bed in your room to five locations in your home, or from your desk at school to five locations around the school. Start by placing a dot for the location of your bed or desk on the left side of the answer area. Then put the locations in order from closest to farthest away. Be sure to label the locations and give the distances to them.

At Home: Find a diagram in a newspaper or magazine. Study the diagram with the student and have him or her interpret it for you.

Name ______________________________

Look up the following words in the dictionary or in the glossary of your reading textbook. For each word, write the part of speech, the definition, and an example of the word in a sentence.

1. rehearse part of speech: ______________

definition: ______________________________

____

example: ______________________________

____

2. cranky part of speech: ______________

definition: ______________________________

example: ______________________________

____

3. specialty part of speech: ______________

definition: ______________________________

____

example: ______________________________

____

4. astronaut part of speech: ______________

definition: ______________________________

example: ______________________________

____

At Home: Play a dictionary game. Invent new words and make up definitions for them.

Name ____________________

Read the following long *i* words. Then use as many of these words as you can in a story that takes place in outer space.

drive	file	kite	wipe	pride	pry	shy
prime	slight	climb	sly	sigh	fright	inside
pies	die	spy	twice	height		

1. First decide on a title for your story. Include at least one long *i* word in your title.

____

2. Now choose two characters to be in your story. Give each character a long *i* name. Write the names below.

____

Write your story on the lines that follow.

____

____

____

____

____

____

____

____

____

At Home: Write a long *i* word, and have the student write as many words as possible below it that fit the same spelling pattern. Then repeat using a different long *i* spelling.

Name ______________________________

Imagine that you are on a rafting trip. Write a journal entry telling about your experiences for one day on the raft. Use each vocabulary word at least once.

raft	scattered	disgusted
nuzzle	downstream	cluttered

Name ______________________________

You are going to write an adventure story. Think about your hero or heroine. List three qualities you will use to define your character and give him or her a name.

____

____

____

What will the setting of your story be?

____

Invent the plot.

Beginning: ______________________________

____

Middle: ______________________________

____

Ending: ______________________________

____

How will your main characters change during the story? Will they make good decisions? Think about how to build excitement through the plot and end with a big finish.

____

____

____

____

On a separate piece of paper, write your story.

At Home: Ask the student to explain to you how the character and setting affect the plot of the story.

Name ______________________________

As you read *The Raft,* fill in the Setting Flow Chart.

Setting

Event	→	Character's Reaction
	→	

Event	→	Character's Reaction
	→	

Event	→	Character's Reaction
	→	

How does the information you wrote in the Setting Flow Chart help you to analyze and make inferences about *The Raft*?

At Home: Have the student use the chart to retell the story.

Name ______________________________

As I read, I will pay attention to the pace and tempo and try to match the action of the story.

Their mother gave them bottles of water and little bags of trail mix.
13 "This way," she called as she headed off.
21 "Slow down!" Nick called out. He wanted to have time to look
33 around. Everything here was so different from the city. The city was
45 **cluttered** with cars, buildings, people, and loud noises. In the woods,
56 there was nothing but trees and the gentle "ssshhhhh" of the wind.
68 Up ahead Nick could see that Felix had reached the edge of the
81 forest and stopped. Beside him was a woman wearing a green uniform.
93 When Nick caught up, his eyes filled with wonder. They were standing
105 on top of a hill made of sand. Below them was the ocean. The air was
121 filled with the salty smell of the water. All around them were more hills
135 of sand. Some were small. Others, like the one they stood on, were huge.
149 Nick felt a little dizzy as he looked down. 158

Comprehension Check

1. What does Nick find interesting about the place he is exploring? **Character, Setting, Plot**

2. How are Nick and Felix different in their approaches to exploring? **Character, Setting, Plot**

	Words Read	–	Number of Errors	=	Words Correct Score
First Read		–		=	
Second Read		–		=	

At Home: Help the student read the passage, paying attention to the goal at the top of the page.

Name ______________________________

Make a map of a park near your house. If there is no park near you, make one up. Create symbols for special features like trails, water fountains, or buildings. Show any bodies of water or unusual land features. Also include a scale with which to measure distances.

At Home: Look at a map with the student. Have him or her use the key and other map features to interpret the map.

Name ______________________________

Choose four difficult words from the selection and write a passage in which you include them, along with context clues. Circle the difficult words. Have a partner underline the context clues.

At Home: Read a paragraph from a book or a magazine, choose a challenging word in it, and have the student point out context clues to its meaning.

Name ____________________

Circle the word with the long *o* sound. Then turn the other word into a long *o* word by adding, taking away, or changing one letter only.

1. grow crown ____________
2. cost told ____________
3. love pole ____________
4. boot float ____________
5. rope fond ____________
6. old could ____________
7. brow slow ____________
8. moat out ____________
9. flow now ____________
10. loud phone ____________
11. shove own ____________
12. tool stone ____________
13. roll gown ____________
14. hope one ____________
15. oven loaf ____________

At Home: Describe an object that is spelled with long *o*. Have the student guess the object and spell its name. Then switch roles.

Name ______________________________

A. Read each word in column 1. Then find a word in column 2 that means the opposite. Write the letter of the word on the line.

1. ______ protested	**a.** artificial
2. ______ trusting	**b.** suspicious
3. ______ endless	**c.** delighted
4. ______ disgusted	**d.** finite
5. ______ natural	**e.** agreed
6. ______ realistic	**f.** unreasonable

B. Write the correct vocabulary words from the box to fill in the blanks.

universe	evidence	consideration	cluttered	raft
sensible	accuse	allergies	astronaut	

7. After much ______________ the coaches decided to call off our game.

8. It was the ______________ thing to do because it was raining buckets.

9. The basement was ______________ with old furniture.

10. The detectives met to discuss ______________ from the investigation.

11. Then it was time to arrest the suspect and ______________ him of car theft.

12. My ______________ were bad because the pollen was high.

13. The ______________ spent two hours repairing the satellite.

14. I felt really small when we were studying the ______________.

15. The survivors built a ______________ and were rescued.

Name ______________________________

Write the correct vocabulary words from the box in the blanks to complete the story.

silken	assignments	eerie	lumbering
wildlife	paralyzed	scattered	consume
roamed	lurk	swallows	completed

Mr. Eardley gives us the best ________________ for science homework! Yesterday we had to watch a documentary on television.

The show was about all kinds of ________________ in the food chain, and I was able to watch them all ________________ their prey close-up! First, you saw a fly caught in a web and the spider rushing over to it. Then the fly slowly became ________________, and the spider wrapped it up in ________________ threads to save it for later.

Next, it showed a herd of zebras that didn't know that lions were closing in to ________________ in the underbrush nearby. Suddenly the lions leaped, and the zebras ________________. Then you saw this lioness ________________ along with a dead zebra hanging out of its mouth, and all the lions were gathering around to feed.

Near the end of the show, it showed a boa constrictor waiting until a baby goat ________________ by and then squeezing it to death. Did you know that a snake ________________ its prey whole? It was really ________________ to watch that! That snake had a big bump in its body and had to rest until digestion was ________________. The boa constrictor was definitely my favorite part!

Name ____

muttered	gaped	insult	snickering
legendary	fluke	flinched	

Write a complete sentence using each vocabulary word. If you can, give your sentences a baseball setting.

1. ____

____

2. ____

____

3. ____

____

4. ____

____

5. ____

____

6. ____

____

7. ____

____

8. Write a sentence using one of the words.

____

Name ___________________________________

An author may write to **entertain**, to **inform**, or to **persuade** the reader.

1. Write a fictional story about baseball to **entertain** the reader. You could write about a Little League game, or the time a fourth grader won an Olympic Gold medal by hitting a home run. Use these or other ideas of your choice. Begin your story in the space below.

2. Think of a subject related to sports that you have a strong opinion about. For example, should baseball be taught as a subject in fourth grade? Is football a better sport than baseball? Should organized sports be part of the school day? Write to **persuade** a reader about your opinion.

At Home: Choose a topic idea. Then, together, think up titles for entertaining, informative, and persuasive pieces about the topic.

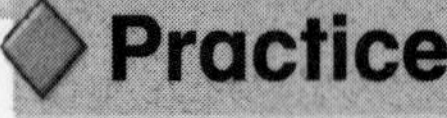

Name ____________________

Comprehension: Author's Purpose

As you read *Mighty Jackie*, fill in the Author's Purpose Map.

Clue	Clue	Clue

Author's Purpose

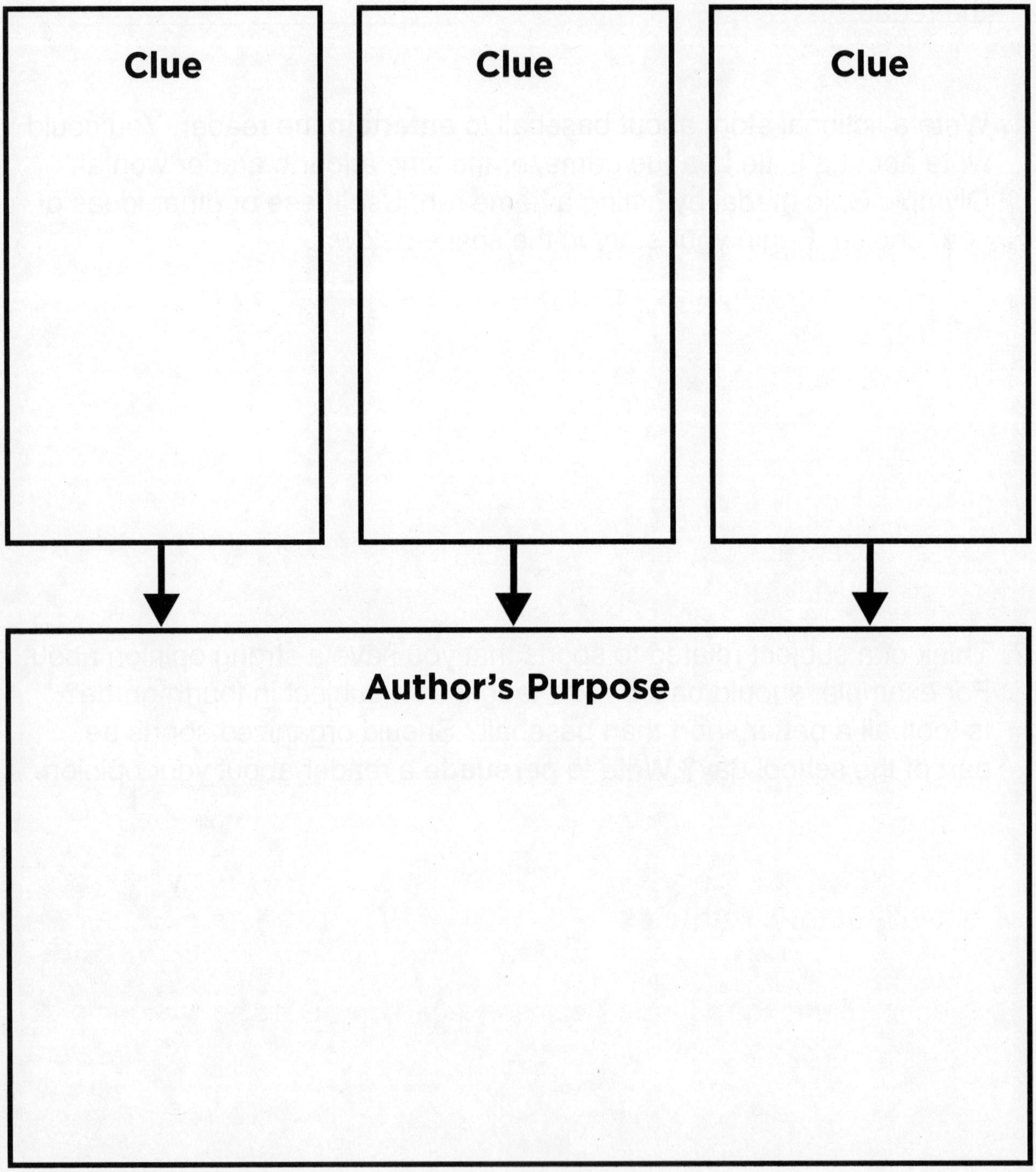

How does the information you wrote in the Author's Purpose Map help you to analyze and make inferences about *Mighty Jackie*?

At Home: Have the student use the chart to retell the story.

Name ______________________________

As I read, I will pay attention to pauses, stops, and intonation.

Jackie Robinson walked toward home plate, swinging
7 his bat. He was in a slump. He just couldn't seem to hit
20 the ball. He couldn't seem to catch it either. His team was
32 expecting more from him. So were the fans in Ebbets Field.
43 After all, he was the first African American player in the
54 major league.
56 As Jackie stepped up to the plate, he couldn't believe
66 what he heard. Insults were flying out of the Philadelphia
76 Phillies dugout.
78 He almost put down his bat and quit the game of
89 baseball forever. Then he thought of his wife Rachel sitting
99 in the stands. He thought of all the people who wanted him
111 to succeed.
113 Planting his feet firmly in the ground, Jackie waited
122 for the pitch. The ball shot toward him and, with a
133 tremendous smack, he sent it into center field. Later, in a
144 daring move, Jackie stole two bases. The fans jumped to
154 their feet. 156

Comprehension Check

1. What lesson do you think the author wants you to take away from this story? **Author's Purpose**

2. What problem does Jackie Robinson face? How does he overcome it? **Problem and Solution**

	Words Read	–	Number of Errors	=	Words Correct Score
First Read		–		=	
Second Read		–		=	

At Home: Help the student read the passage, paying attention to the goal at the top of the page.

Name ______________________________

Text Feature: Table

Make a table to display information from two games of your grade's softball team. In the first game, your team had 12 hits, scored 5 runs, walked 3 times, struck out 5 times, and made 1 error. In the second game, your team had 17 hits, scored 8 runs, walked 6 times, struck out 2 times, and made 3 errors.

Give your team a name, and include it in a title for the table.

At Home: Help the student make a simple table to display information on weather, sports, or other information.

Name ______________________________

When you read an unfamiliar word, **context clues** may help you figure out what it means. Read the entire sentence, and sentences nearby, to see if you can find clues to the meaning of the word.

Write sentences using the following words from the story *Mighty Jackie.* Include clues that would help someone understand the meaning of the word. For example, using the word *mighty* from the title, you might write: "Jackie was a mighty pitcher. She pitched so well that she struck out two famous major leaguers."

1. exhibition ______________________________

____

2. insult ______________________________

____

3. glared ______________________________

____

4. bleachers ______________________________

____

5. jeering ______________________________

____

6. sandlot ______________________________

____

At Home: As the student reads at home, ask him or her to find words that are explained in context. List these words and the clues that helped define them.

Practice

Name ________________________________

Phonics: *ch* and *tch*

Think about words you know with ***ch*** or ***tch***. Some words, like *champion*, have the ***ch*** at the beginning. Others, like *watchful*, have ***tch*** in the middle of the word. Another set of ***ch*** or ***tch*** words have the sound at the end, as in *watch or such*.

On the lines below, list three ch **or** tch **words for each category.**

Beginning	Middle	End
________	________	________
________	________	________
________	________	________

Write a story using the words in your list. Try to include all of the words you listed.

____

____

____

____

____

____

____

____

____

At Home: Help the student make up a crossword or word-search puzzle that uses *ch* words and *tch* words. Challenge a family member to solve the puzzle.

Name ______________________________

overheard	opportunities	boycotts	citizen
unions	strikes	border	

Make your own crossword puzzle using the vocabulary words above. Remember to start with *Across* clues and then give the *Down* clues. Then draw numbered boxes for the answers. Exchange your puzzle with a partner and try to solve his or her puzzle.

Across

____

____

____

____

Down

____

____

____

____

Write sentences using each of these words: *strikes, boycotts,* and *unions.*

____

____

____

____

____

____

____

Name ________________________________

Read the following sentences from "My Diary from Here to There." Make an inference from each one. Use what you already know from the story along with what the sentence says.

1. "How can I sleep knowing we might leave Mexico forever?"
   Make an inference about how Amada feels.

   ____

   ____

   ____

2. "We each picked out a smooth, heart-shaped stone to remind us always of our friendship."
   Make an inference about the way Amada and Michi feel.

   ____

   ____

   ____

3. "Mamá held Mario and our green cards close to her heart."
   Make an inference about how Mamá feels.

   ____

   ____

   ____

4. "Tío Tito keeps trying to make us laugh instead of cry."
   Make an inference about the feelings of Amada's family.

   ____

   ____

   ____

At Home: Describe a fictional person's behavior. Ask the student to make an inference about the character's mood based on your description. Then trade roles.

Name ______________________________

As you read *My Diary from Here to There*, fill in the Inferences Word Web.

Clue

Clue

Inference

Clue

Clue

Clue

Clue

Inference

Clue

Clue

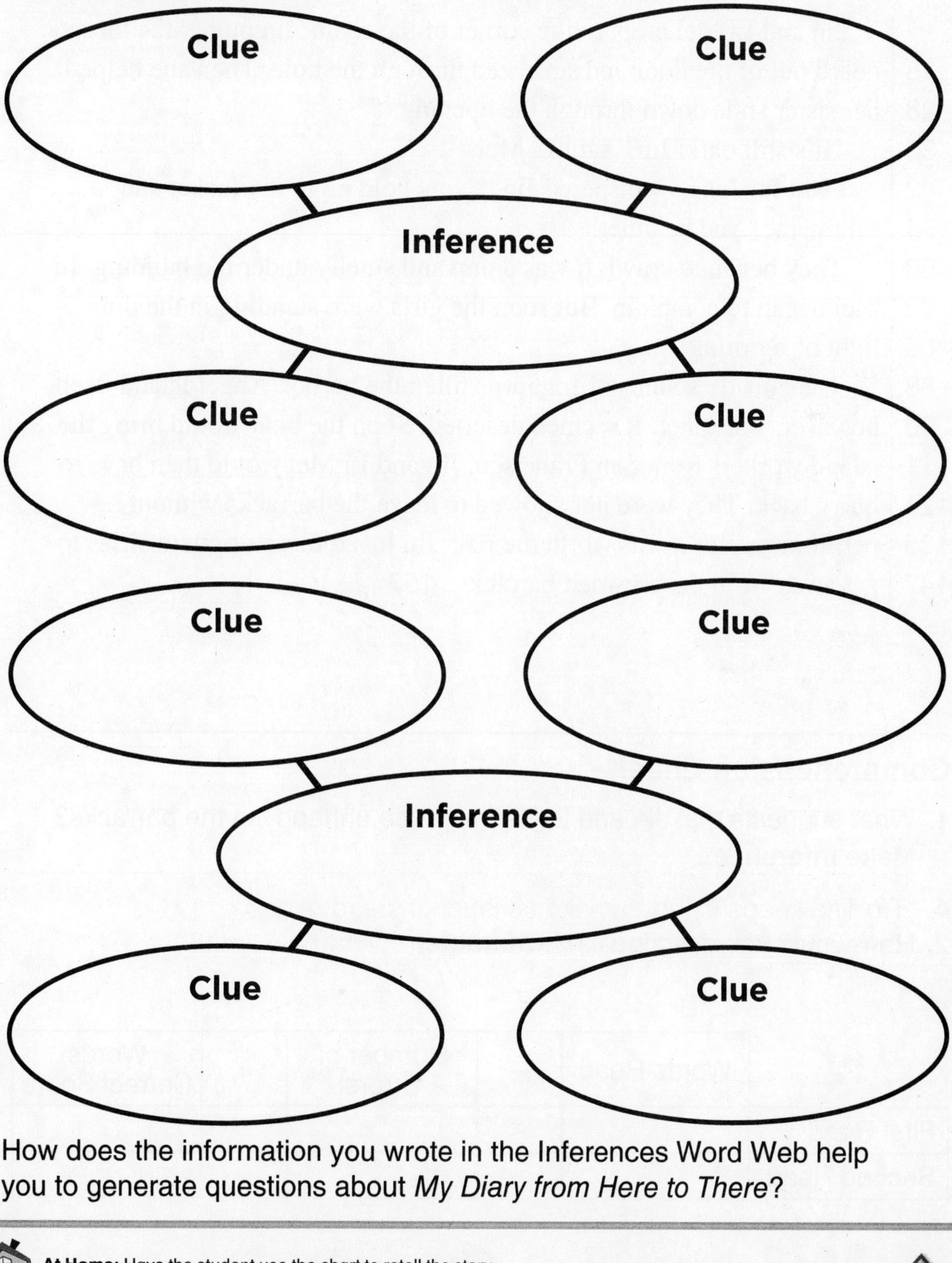

How does the information you wrote in the Inferences Word Web help you to generate questions about *My Diary from Here to There*?

At Home: Have the student use the chart to retell the story.

Name ____

As I read, I will pay attention to end punctuation in each sentence.

Jin and Li Mei crept to the corner of the room. Jin pulled the loose
15 board out of the floor and squeezed through the hole. Then she helped
28 her sister slide down through the opening.
35 "It's still dark, Jin," said Li Mei.
42 "Not for long," whispered Jin. "Now hold on to my jacket and
54 follow me. And be quiet!"
59 They began to crawl. It was damp and smelly under the building. Li
72 Mei began to complain. But soon the girls were standing in the dim
85 light of morning.
88 The ghostly sounds of foghorns filled the harbor. Angel Island itself,
99 however, was quiet. It seemed deserted. Soon the boat would bring the
111 island workers from San Francisco. Jin and Li Mei would then have to
124 hurry back. They were not allowed to leave the barracks without
135 permission. But it was worth the risk. Jin loved these **opportunities** to
147 get away from the crowded barracks. 153

Comprehension Check

1. What suggests that Jin and Li Mei might be unhappy in the barracks? **Make Inferences**

2. How would you describe Jin? **Character**

	Words Read	–	Number of Errors	=	Words Correct Score
First Read		–		=	
Second Read		–		=	

At Home: Help the student read the passage, paying attention to the goal at the top of the page.

Name ____

Read the following primary source. It is an autobiographical sketch of a Chinese immigrant named Lee Chew, who came from China to the United States in the early 1900s.

My father gave me $100, and I went to Hong Kong with five other boys from our place and we got steerage passage on a steamer, paying $50 each. Everything was new to me. All my life I had been used to sleeping on a board bed with a wooden pillow, and I found the steamer's bunk very uncomfortable because it was so soft. The food was different from that which I had been used to, and I did not like it at all. . . .

When I got to San Francisco . . . I was half starved. . . . but a few days' living in the Chinese quarter made me happy again. A man got me work as a house servant in an American family, and my start was the same as that of almost all the Chinese in this country.

What kinds of things can you learn about immigration from this story? What kinds of things can you not learn?

____

____

____

____

____

____

____

____

____

At Home: Ask the student about primary sources. What sorts of things can they tell us about the past?

Name ____________________

The **origins** or **history** of a word can help you to understand it. Many words came into our language from other languages or have changed from what they used to mean.

microphone *noun*. a device that changes sound waves into electrical signals. *I was glad the microphone was working when I addressed the assembly.*

word history: Microphone comes from two Greek words that mean "very small" and "sound."

Use your dictionary to find the word histories of four words that interest you. Write down what you learn in the form of the sample entry above.

1. ____________________

____

____

2. ____________________

____

____

3. ____________________

____

____

4. ____________________

____

____

At Home: Discuss the history of the student's name with him or her.

Name ______________________________

Write as many words that you can think of using the consonant diagraphs below. Be sure to use each in the beginning, middle, and end position of the words where you can.

th: ______________________________

____

sh: ______________________________

____

wh: ______________________________

____

ph: ______________________________

____

Now write three sentences that each use at least two of the words you wrote above.

____

____

____

____

____

____

At Home: Have the student create a sentence that includes all four of these sounds: *sh*, *ph*, *wh*, and *th*.

Name ______________________________

temples	dynasties	heritage	preserve	overjoyed

Show your understanding of the vocabulary words by using each one in a sentence. For an extra challenge, link the sentences together into a story.

1. ______________________________

____

2. ______________________________

____

3. ______________________________

____

4. ______________________________

____

5. ______________________________

____

Name ____

Facts and **opinions** are very different, but you need both to be able to persuade someone. In the following paragraph, the writer uses two facts to support her opinion.

Fact Our town's landfill will run out of room in less than ten years. Shipping our garbage out of the area is becoming more expensive. For both of these reasons, I believe that we should act now to increase the amount of trash that we recycle. **Opinion**

Write a short paragraph of your own on a subject related to your school or neighborhood. State an opinion and support it with at least two facts. Label the facts and opinion.

____

____

____

____

____

____

____

____

____

____

____

____

At Home: Listen to TV or radio news reports or read magazine articles on topics that interest both you and the student. Discuss what facts and opinions are included.

Name ______________________________

As you read *Stealing Beauty,* fill in the Fact and Opinion Chart.

Fact	Opinion

How does the information you wrote in the Fact and Opinion Chart help you to analyze and make inferences about *Stealing Beauty*?

At Home: Have the student use the chart to retell the story.

Name ______________________________

As I read, I will pay attention to tempo.

You have just arrived by boat at a city on a great river.
13 The town is built on a cliff high above the riverbank. You
25 walk up 300 steps from the dock to reach the city gate.
36 The gate is built into the city's old stone wall. A nearby
48 market sells everything from pears to high-heeled shoes.
56 Near the city gate is a terrace. There are tables and
67 chairs where you can sit and look out over the mighty river
79 below. In the distance is the entrance to a magnificent gorge.
90 The cliffs of the river canyon rise steeply into the sky.
101 Boats look small from where you sit.
108 This is the town of Fengjie (FUNG-jee), China. It is
117 on the banks of the Yangtze (YANK-see) River, the longest
126 river in all of Asia. But Fengjie won't be here much longer.
138 By the year 2009, the entire town will be under water. 148

Comprehension Check

1. When the author states that Fengjie will not be here in 2009, is that a fact or an opinion? **Fact and Opinion**

2. Name three details from the first paragraph which support the idea that Fengjie is an old city that has not seen many modern changes. **Main Idea and Detail**

	Words Read	–	Number of Errors	=	Words Correct Score
First Read		–		=	
Second Read		–		=	

At Home: Help the student read the passage, paying attention to the goal at the top of the page.

Practice

Study Skill: Parts of a Book

Name ____

Suppose that you had a chance to design a book on China. What topics would you cover? How would you organize them? Below, write a table of contents for your book. Include at least five chapter titles, a glossary and an index. Give the page number where each would begin.

____ ____

____ ____

____ ____

____ ____

____ ____

____ ____

____ ____

____ ____

At Home: Together, examine the back cover and other parts of some of the student's books. Discuss how they are the same and how they are different.

Name ______________________________

You have learned three rules for making plurals. In the exercises below, state the rule to follow to make that word plural. Then show the plural, and give two other words to which the same rule applies.

1. watch Rule: ______________________________

____

Plural: ______________

Two more examples: ______________ ______________

2. country Rule: ______________________________

____

Plural: ______________

Two more examples: ______________ ______________

3. road Rule: ______________________________

Plural: ______________

Two more examples: ______________ ______________

At Home: Have the student explain the plural formation rules that he or she created.

Name ____________________

Practice

Phonics: Three-Consonant Clusters

Peel back the "onion" of the word ***split,*** and you can find the short, rhyming words ***slit, pit, lit, sit.*** Or peel the word ***straps*** and find ***traps, taps, raps, saps.***

Choose four other words that begin with a three-consonant cluster like *shr, thr, spr, scr,* and *spl.* Then peel shorter, rhyming words from the original word.

1. Original word: ____________________

Rhyming words: ____________________ ____________________

____

2. Original word: ____________________

Rhyming words: ____________________ ____________________

____

3. Original word: ____________________

Rhyming words: ____________________ ____________________

____

4. Original word: ____________________

Rhyming words: ____________________ ____________________

____

At Home: Pick a three-consonant cluster like *shr, thr, spr, scr,* or *spl.* Have the student identify as many words containing the cluster as he or she can within one minute.

Name ______________________________

Think of something you'd like to invent. Your invention might make life easier, or it might be just for fun. Then write a paragraph advertising your invention. Use each vocabulary word.

hilarious	handy	nowadays	independence
convinced	dizzy	whirlwind	mischief

____

____

____

____

____

____

____

____

____

____

____

____

____

____

____

Name ________________________________

Read each problem. Then write a creative solution that solves it.

1. **Problem:** Jason's cat keeps pouncing on his school papers and tearing them. What can Jason do?

   Solution: ________________________________

   ____

2. **Problem:** Carmela is scheduled to be at play rehearsal and a soccer practice at the same time. What should she do?

   Solution: ________________________________

   ____

Now make up problems to fit the following solutions.

3. **Solution:** Jean can go next door and ask her neighbor, who used to work at City Hall.

   Problem: ________________________________

   ____

   ____

   ____

4. **Solution:** Kia can write a list of instructions and tape them to the refrigerator.

   Problem: ________________________________

   ____

   ____

   ____

At Home: Think of a problem and ask the student to solve it. Then trade roles and have the student tell you a problem that you must solve.

Name ____

As you read *How Ben Franklin Stole the Lightning*, fill in the Problem and Solution Chart.

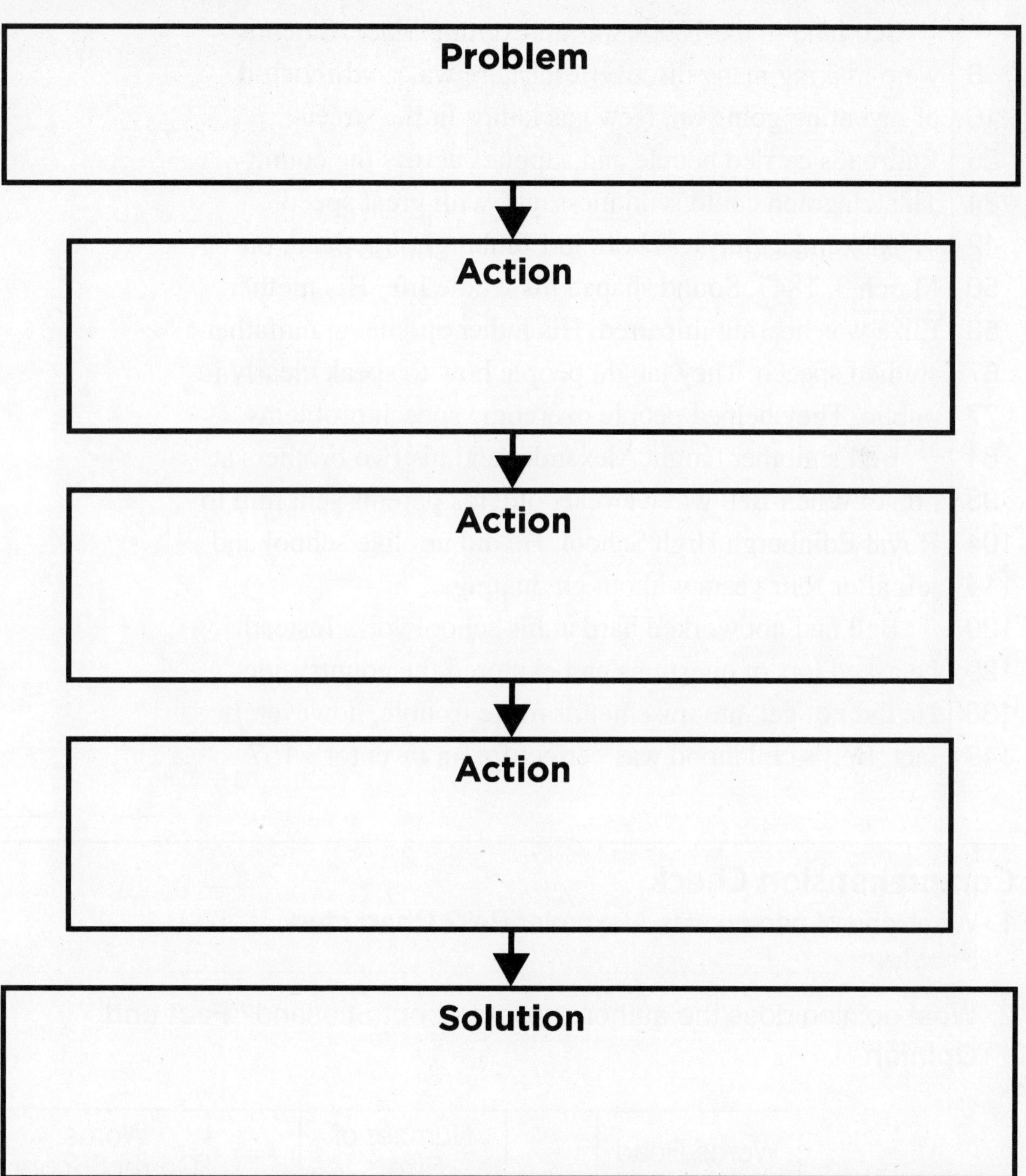

How does the information you wrote in the Problem and Solution Chart help you to generate questions about *How Ben Franklin Stole the Lightning*?

At Home: Have the student use the chart to retell the story.

As I read, I will pay attention to match my tempo with the energy of the passage.

Scotland in the 1800s was an exciting place. Scientists
8 were making many discoveries. There was a **whirlwind**
16 of inventing going on. New gas lamps lit the streets.
26 Railroads carried people and supplies across the country.
34 The telegraph could send messages with great speed.
42 Alexander Bell was born in Edinburgh, Scotland, on
50 March 3, 1847. Sound shaped his whole life. His mother
58 Eliza was hearing impaired. His father and his grandfather
67 studied speech. They taught people how to speak clearly in
77 public. They helped people overcome speech problems.
84 Bell's mother taught Alexander and his two brothers at
93 home. When Bell was 11 years old, his parents sent him to
104 Royal Edinburgh High School. He did not like school and
114 left after four years without graduating.
120 Bell had not worked hard at his schoolwork. Instead
129 he asked lots of questions and explored the countryside.
138 He did not get into mischief or make trouble, however. In
149 fact, Bell's childhood was perfect for an inventor! 157

Comprehension Check

1. What kind of person was Alexander Bell? **Character**

2. What opinion does the author express about Scotland? **Fact and Opinion**

	Words Read	–	Number of Errors	=	Words Correct Score
First Read		–		=	
Second Read		–		=	

At Home: Help the student read the passage, paying attention to the goal at the top of the page.

Name ______________________________

Write at least one piece of figurative language for each of the items below.

1. sour milk ______________________________
2. art class ______________________________
3. new bicycle ______________________________
4. hot popcorn ______________________________
5. so ugly ______________________________
6. oops a skunk ______________________________
7. the best birthday present ______________________________
8. the play that won the game ______________________________

Now choose one of the items above to begin creating a poem of 4 to 8 lines. Visualize your subject and play with vivid words, including the figurative language you wrote above. Then tie together strings of words with alliteration.

____

____

____

____

____

As your poem starts coming together, think about where you would like the poem to rhyme. Perhaps you would prefer to write a poem without rhyme. Organize your poem on a separate sheet of paper and rewrite the final version to give to your teacher.

At Home: Point to objects around your home and together, come up with phrases using alliteration to describe each one.

Practice

Name ______________________________

Vocabulary Strategy: Idioms

In the blanks below, write the letter of the definition that best matches each idiom.

1. ____ as the crow flies
2. ____ eat crow
3. ____ for the birds
4. ____ My goose is cooked.
5. ____ a feather in my cap
6. ____ under my wing
7. ____ fly in the ointment
8. ____ bee in my bonnet

a. something that I keep thinking about
b. worthless, ridiculous
c. something to be proud of
d. in my care
e. make a difficult apology
f. drawback, problem
g. in a straight line from place to place
h. I'm in trouble.

Use as many of these idioms in a passage below.

____

____

____

____

____

____

____

____

At Home: Discuss the meanings of the idioms above with the student.

Name ______________________________

Complete the word ladders below. Changing only one letter at a time, transform the starting word to the finishing word. Each change must result in a real word. Do not rearrange letters, and do not replace the *r*.

1. farm
   ____
   harp
   ____

2. park
   ____
   ____
   fort

3. barn
   ____
   dark
   ____

4. score
   ____
   ____
   shark

Now create two word ladders of your own.

5. ______________
   ____
   ____
   ____

6. ______________
   ____
   ____
   ____

At Home: See how many words spelled with */är/* or */ôr/* the student can think of in one minute.

Name ________________________________

Sometimes we associate words with pictures in our minds. For example, you might think of birds flying if you hear the word *flock.* Describe a picture that you might associate with each vocabulary word below.

1. slithered ________________________________
2. apologize ________________________________
3. ambulance ________________________________
4. cardboard ________________________________
5. weekdays ________________________________
6. genuine ________________________________
7. harmless ________________________________

Choose one of the words above and write a paragraph describing the image that came to mind with vivid words.

____

____

____

____

____

Name ______________________________

Read the passage and make inferences to answer the questions that follow.

Elena Serna Tinao was awake before her alarm clock rang. Still, after getting only about five hours of sleep, Elena bounded out of bed and dressed quickly.

Grabbing her sleeping bag, her hiking boots, her guidebook about the Grand Canyon, and her packed duffel bag, Elena shuffled to the front door and set everything down. "Should I wake up the rest of the family now, or wait ten more minutes?" she asked herself.

1. What is Elena doing?

a. preparing to leave for a school trip

b. preparing to leave on a family outing

c. preparing eggs and bacon

2. Where is Elena going?

a. to the Grand Canyon

b. to the kitchen

c. to a sleepover at Pam's house

3. What will Elena probably do there?

a. wake up her family

b. read the guidebook

c. go camping and hiking

4. How does Elena feel this morning?

a. anxious

b. sleepy

c. contented

5. Why did Elena get only five hours of sleep?

a. She watched too much television.

b. The guidebook was so fascinating.

c. She had trouble falling asleep.

6. What would be the wisest thing to do next?

a. wake up the family

b. wait ten minutes, then wake up the family

c. read the guide book until everyone is ready

At Home: Have the student read a story and make inferences about the behaviors and motivations of the characters.

Name ______________________________

As you read *Dear Mr. Winston,* fill in the Inferences Word Web.

Inference

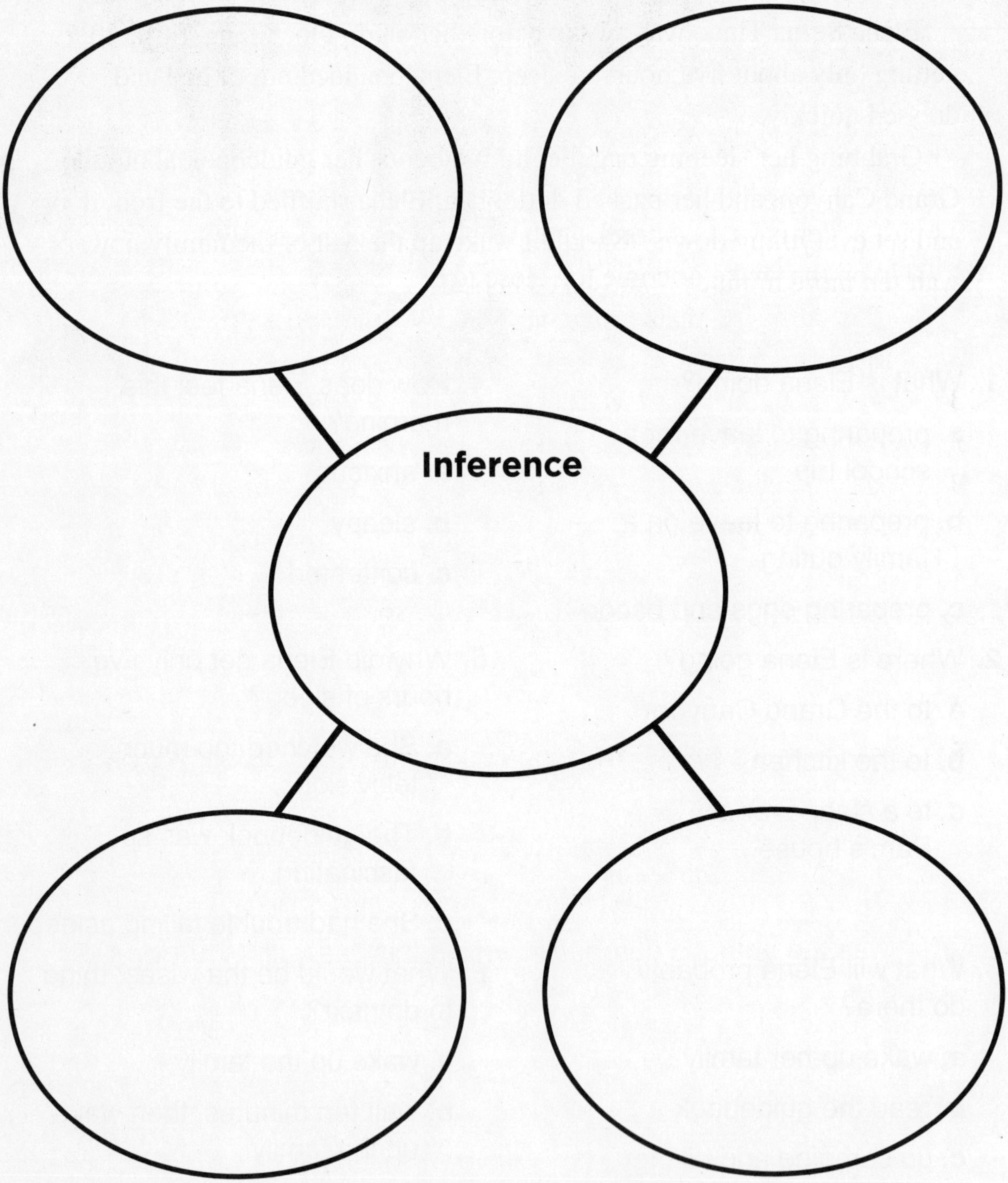

How does the information you wrote in the Inferences Word Web help you to generate questions about *Dear Mr. Winston*?

At Home: Have the student use the chart to retell the story.

Name ____________________

As I read, I will pay attention to tempo.

The puff adder is one of Africa's most common
9 venomous snakes. It can be found in dry areas like
19 woodlands, low forests, and grasslands all across Africa.
27 But it is hard to find. Its light brown, green, and black skin
40 camouflages it very well. The puff adder also blends in
50 with its habitat among rocks and fallen trees. Because the
60 puff adder is well camouflaged, people often accidentally
68 step on the snake or come too close to it.
78 The puff adder can remain motionless for long periods
87 of time. Because of this its prey and enemies often come
98 very close to the snake without realizing it. Within
107 seconds the puff adder can strike. It puffs up its head and
119 makes a loud hissing sound before it attacks. The puff
129 adder moves forward in a straight line instead of slithering
139 from side to side. This helps it dart even more quickly at
152 nearby prey like rodents, toads, and other snakes. 160

Comprehension Check

1. Explain why there are so many puff adders in Africa. **Make Inferences**

2. What was the author's purpose in writing this passage? **Author's Purpose**

	Words Read	–	Number of Errors	=	Words Correct Score
First Read		–		=	
Second Read		–		=	

At Home: Help the student read the passage, paying attention to the goal at the top of the page.

Name ______________________________

Electronic encyclopedias contain articles on many subjects. You can find information in them by accessing the **toolbars**. The **toolbars** are usually located at the top of the screen. Use your mouse to open a toolbar. Inside you will find items to click that will move you to different parts of the encyclopedia.

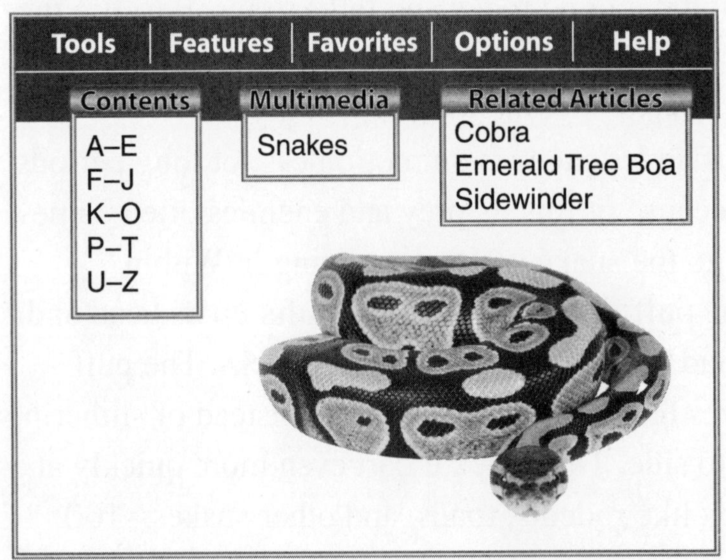

Answer these questions about the electronic encyclopedia above.

Which **toolbar** would you click to learn:

1. about garter snakes? ____________________
2. about the sidewinder? ____________________
3. if there are any films about cobras? ____________________
4. more detailed information about the Emerald Tree Boa?

____

5. how many kinds of rattlesnakes there are? ____________________
6. how to navigate through the encyclopedia? ____________________

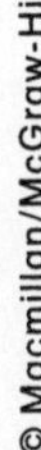

At Home: Play a keyword game with the student. Take turns thinking of research topics and identifying good keywords for them.

Name ______________________________

From the table below, pick a base word and a prefix or suffix (or both). The combination must be an existing word. Write your words and their meanings on the lines below.

Prefixes	Base Words	Suffixes
pre-	adventure	-y or -ly
un-	pay	-ous
in-	green	-ing
anti-	help	-ish
dis-	creep	-ful
	comfortable	
	please	
	definite	
	violent	

1. Word: ______________

Definition: ______________________________

2. Word: ______________

Definition: ______________________________

3. Word: ______________

Definition: ______________________________

4. Word: ______________

Definition: ______________________________

5. Word: ______________

Definition: ______________________________

At Home: Have the student explain the meanings of the words that he or she created.

Name ___________________________________

Complete the story by filling in the blanks with words that have the *air, are, ear,* and *ere* spellings. The letters in parentheses are clues that form part of each answer.

On the Train

LaToya was taking the train with her brother, Mark. They were on the way to their grandparents' horse farm. Their (m) ________________ had just had a new colt.

"I wish we could have flown in an ________________ (plane)," complained LaToya. "Then we could have gotten there yesterday. Isn't there an ________________ (port) in the ________________ (ea)?

"I'm afraid there isn't one (n) ________________ the ranch," said Mark. "Besides we wouldn't want to inconvenience our (d) ________________ grandparents. Only a (m) ________________ staff of seven workers (sh) ________________ all the chores as it is."

LaToya (st) ________________ (ed) out the window, becoming (aw) ________________ of someone waving. "Look," she said. "Isn't that Grandfather's pickup truck pulling into the station?"

"That's Grandpa, all right!" Mark exclaimed. "I'd know that truck (anywh) ________________! Let's get our (g) ________________ and go meet him on the platform! Be (c) ________________ (ful) on the (s) ________________ (s) , LaToya. Don't run!" Mark called after his sister.

At Home: Talk with the student about other spellings for the /âr/ and /îr/ sounds.

Name ____________________

legendary	snickering	fluke	opportunities
citizen	overheard	hilarious	heritage
nowadays	mischief	dynasties	
apologize	ambulance	genuine	

Choose ten vocabulary words from the box above. Write a sentence for each word, leaving a blank space where the vocabulary word should be. Exchange your sentences with a partner. Fill in the blanks for each other's sentences.

1. ____________________
2. ____________________
3. ____________________
4. ____________________
5. ____________________
6. ____________________
7. ____________________
8. ____________________
9. ____________________
10. ____________________

Name ______________________________

Draw pictures to represent six words from the box. Exchange pictures with a classmate. Try to identify the word represented by each picture.

gaped	overheard	hilarious	whirlwind	slithered
dizzy	border	temples	overjoyed	preserve
genuine	harmless	ambulance	weekdays	legendary

Name ______________________________

interfere	guardian	awkward
agile	proclaimed	tottered

Use the rhyming clues to help you identify the correct vocabulary word for each blank.

1. The teacher made it very clear that we should let them argue and not

   ________________.

2. The ballerina may look gangly and fragile, but when she dances she's

   very ________________.

3. "I heard the news," my friend exclaimed. "This is the law that the king

   ________________."

4. The baby ________________, with steps uneven. "Dad, hurry! Catch Stephen!"

5. I tried to do the crossword, with my sprained hand, but my

   ________________ writing was hard to understand.

6. Mr. Horatio Clive Carbuncle is not my ________________ but my uncle.

Write a sentence of your own that uses three of the vocabulary words.

____

____

____

Practice

Name ______________________

Comprehension: Author's Purpose

Usually authors write to **entertain,** to **inform,** or to **persuade.**

Write two sentences that might be from a folk tale involving talking animals with the purpose being to entertain a reader. Follow them with two sentences that inform a reader of facts about animals. Then finally, write two sentences that persuade a reader to donate money to feed hungry animals.

1. Entertaining sentences:

____

____

____

____

2. Informational sentences:

____

____

____

____

3. Persuasive sentences:

____

____

____

____

At Home: Read an opinion column or a letter to the editor with the student. How does the writer achieve his or her purpose of persuading readers?

Name ___________________________

As you read *Roadrunner's Dance,* fill in the Author's Purpose Map.

Clue	Clue	Clue

Author's Purpose

How does the information you wrote in the Author's Purpose Map help you to evaluate *Roadrunner's Dance*?

At Home: Have the student use the chart to retell the story.

Name ____________________

As I read, I will pay attention to pauses, stops, intonation, and characters' words.

Far away, in a land of ice and snow, there lived a father, a mother, and
16 their young son. The boy was small for his age. Everyone in the village
30 called him Miki, which meant "little" in the Inupiac language.
40 One day, Miki's father and his uncle went north to hunt. They were
53 gone for many long days, and Miki and his mother began to worry. At
67 long last, Miki's uncle returned. But he was alone and empty-handed. He
79 insisted that something had taken his brother away in the dark of night.
92 But he could not tell Miki or his mother what kind of creature had carried
107 him away. No footprints had been left behind.
115 He said, "The North Wind must have covered the footprints with snow.
127 Or maybe the North Wind itself blew my brother away. Either way, he
140 will never return."
143 Miki and his mother did not give up hope. They knew in their hearts
157 that the father could still be alive. They watched and waited for him. But
171 there came a time when there was no food and it was left to Miki to
187 provide for the family. It was a big responsibility for such a small boy. 201

Comprehension Check

1. How can you tell that Miki and his mother do not believe the uncle? **Make Inferences**

2. What has occurred in the plot to change the lives of the characters? **Character, Plot, Setting**

	Words Read	–	Number of Errors	=	Words Correct Score
First Read		–		=	
Second Read		–		=	

At Home: Help the student read the passage, paying attention to the goal at the top of the page.

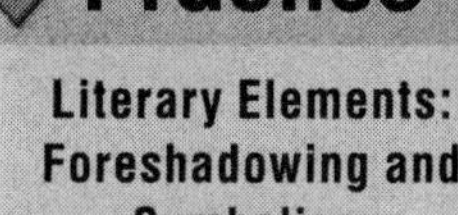

Name ______________________________

Read the passage. Then continue the story on the blank lines below it. Make sure that the finished story has both foreshadowing and symbolism.

Preston looked down in confusion at the three dried pumpkin seeds in the palm of his hand and cried, "You're sending me into the Dreaded Swamp and across the Sea of No Return and for my protection you're giving me pumpkin seeds!"

Preston's fairy godfather hastened to calm him. "But these are no ordinary seeds, my boy. Just poke one of these into the soil whenever you find yourself in danger and the perfect solution will sprout within seconds. With these in your possession, Preston, you cannot fail."

____

____

____

____

____

____

____

____

____

____

____

____

____

At Home: Have the student read his story to you. Discuss the foreshadowing and symbolism. Talk with him or her about the tale's lesson.

Name ______________________________

One common use of synonyms may be seen every day in your newspaper's crossword puzzle. Write synonyms of the words below in the crossword puzzle boxes. Put one letter in each box. Use capital letters to write each word.

DOWN

1. meddle
2. uncoordinated

ACROSS

3. wobbled
4. defender
5. nimble
6. made a declaration

At Home: Have the student create an original crossword puzzle and use synonyms as clues for the words.

Name ______________________________

In words like ***twirl, urn, person,*** and ***learn,*** the vowel + ***r*** combination makes the sound /ûr/.

On the lines below, write at least three examples that follow each of the patterns. Make sure that the word makes the /ûr/ sound. For example, *search* makes the /ûr/ sound, but *fear* does not.

ir* as in *twirl	***ur* as in *urn***	***er* as in *person***	***ear* as in *learn***
________	________	________	________
________	________	________	________
________	________	________	________
________	________	________	________
________	________	________	________

Now use as many of the words you wrote as possible in a paragraph. Circle the words with the /ûr/ sound.

____

____

____

____

____

At Home: Ask the student to come up with examples of words that follow the above spelling patterns, but that do not make the /ûr/ sound.

Name ______________________________

injustice	ancestors	unfair	avoided
numerous	unsuspecting	segregation	

Use each pair of vocabulary words in a single sentence.

1. unfair, injustice

____

____

2. segregation, avoided

____

____

3. numerous, unsuspecting

____

____

4. ancestors, unfair

____

____

List the vocabulary words under the correct part of speech.

Noun	Verb	Adjective
________	________	________
________	________	________
________	________	________

Name ______________________________

Decide whether the sentences below were written to inform or persuade. Write the author's purpose on the blank. Then rewrite the sentence to achieve a different purpose.

Example: The car had a big engine and could go very fast.

inform

Don't buy big cars with big engines because they waste gasoline and they are dangerous. persuade

1. Dr. Martin Luther King was a hero who turned the world upside down because he spoke out for his people. ______________

____

____

2. In the segregated South, African Americans could not use some hotels and were sent to separate schools. ______________

____

____

3. Rosa Parks is the most famous Civil Rights activist because she was the first person to take action. ______________

____

____

4. Christine's family did not use the elevator at the city hall because it had a sign that said "Whites Only." ______________

____

____

At Home: Have the student write a persuasive paragraph. Then analyze which sentences give facts and which sentences attempt to persuade.

Name ______________________________

As you read *My Brother Martin,* fill in the Author's Purpose Map.

Clue	Clue	Clue

↓ ↓ ↓

Author's Purpose

How does the information you wrote in the Author's Purpose Map help you to evaluate *My Brother Martin*?

At Home: Have the student use the chart to retell the story.

Name ______________________________

As I read, I will pay attention to punctuation in each sentence.

In the early 1800s women in the United States had few
11 rights. Women could only hold a few types of jobs. They
22 could teach or work in factories. They couldn't be doctors
32 or lawyers. A woman made less money than a man who
43 had the same type of job. And most important of all,
54 women couldn't vote.
57 When a woman married, all her property became her
66 husband's. Wives had to ask their husbands for spending
75 money. If a woman divorced, her children stayed with her
85 husband. A husband owned everything.
90 By the mid-1800s some people decided it was time to
100 change the way women were treated. Two of those people
110 were Susan B. Anthony and Elizabeth Cady Stanton. They
119 both thought women should be able to vote and have the
130 same rights as men. They worked hard to change the laws
141 and the way people thought.
146 Elizabeth Cady Stanton was born in 1815. Her mother's
154 ancestors were wealthy and well known. Her father worked
163 hard. He studied law and worked in politics. 171

Comprehension Check

1. Why do you think the author wrote about Susan B. Anthony and Elizabeth Cady Stanton? **Author's Purpose**

2. Why did these women want to change the laws? **Make Inferences**

	Words Read	–	Number of Errors	=	Words Correct Score
First Read		–		=	
Second Read		–		=	

At Home: Help the student read the passage, paying attention to the goal at the top of the page.

Name ___________________________

Write a letter to someone you feel has made a difference to our world. The person doesn't have to be famous. Include a salutation in your letter. In the body of the letter, tell the person why you think he or she made a difference, and ask a question or questions. End your letter with a complimentary closing and sign your name.

At Home: Have the student compare and contrast letters and emails.

Name ____

Un- and ***re-*** are very useful prefixes, capable of changing the meanings of all kinds of words. But don't just take our word for it—try it yourself.

Use *un-* and *re-* to create five new words in the lines below. Define each new word and use it in a sentence.

1. discover Prefix-: ____________ Meaning: ____________________
Sentence:

____

2. believable Prefix-: ____________ Meaning: ____________________
Sentence:

____

3. healthy Prefix-: ____________ Meaning: ____________________
Sentence:

____

4. construct Prefix-: ____________ Meaning: ____________________
Sentence:

____

5. identified Prefix-: ____________ Meaning: ____________________
Sentence:

____

At Home: Have the student explain the new words that he or she created.

Name ______________________________

Certain combinations of letters often have one silent letter. Among these are ***wr*** (silent ***w***), ***kn*** (silent ***k***), ***lm*** (silent ***l***), and ***mb*** (silent ***b***).

In the blanks below, write a total of twenty words that include one of the silent letters above. Be sure to write each word under the correct heading.

wr	kn	lm	mb
______	______	______	______
______	______	______	______
______	______	______	______
______	______	______	______
______	______	______	______
______	______	______	______

Use as many of the words that you found as possible to create a short passage. You may choose to write a nonfiction article or the beginning or ending to a work of fiction.

____

____

____

____

____

____

____

At Home: Have the student write a sentence that uses as many silent letters as he or she can fit into it.

Name ______________________________

identified   enterprising   persistence   venture

Read the passage, then answer the questions that follow. Be sure to use the vocabulary word in your answer.

The whole week before the big game, Juan had butterflies in his stomach. He set time aside after school each day to practice with Lamar and prepare for the approaching game.

On the day of the game, the team felt ready. It was the bottom of the ninth. Bases were loaded. The pitch came at Juan fast, low, and inside. Even in his sleep, Juan stepped into the pitch and swung. *Whack!* The ball went all the way to the wall, and all his teammates ran home! Now it was a tie game, with Juan himself on third . . . .

Lamar stepped up to the plate and hit a home run!

1. Juan **identified** a need to do something. What was it?

____

2. How does Juan show **persistence** in the passage?

____

3. Do you think Juan might approach another **venture** in his life the same way?

____

4. What proves that Juan and Lamar were **enterprising?**

____

Read the following adapted book review.

The first book of this popular series introduces readers to an orphan and the tattered remains of his newfound family. Jonathan Warble loses his parents at a young age.

When his parents' will is read (in Chapter Two), he finds himself rich beyond his wildest dreams. However, he can't put his hands on the money until he is much older. Until then, he is placed in the care of his great-aunt Alice Mary Beth Grabbal-Andrun, a person from the other side of the family.

Aunt Alice Mary Beth and Jonathan have little to discuss. The great-aunt was a concert violinist and Jonathan plays electric guitar. Feelings of grief in both struggle against any happiness. But while Jonathan grieves for his parents, his aunt pines for their money.

The situation goes on like this forever. Many things happen—stilted conversations, awful food, an interesting concert, a couple of spiteful cousins. After years and years, Jonathan finally gets the money and Aunt Alice Mary Beth doesn't. So everything turns out all right in the end.

Think about the characters described in the review. In what ways are they alike? In what ways are they different? Fill in the chart below. You may have to use a separate sheet of paper.

Alike	Different
1.	1.
2.	2.
3.	3.
4.	4.

At Home: Take turns with the student in comparing and contrasting characters on television programs.

Name ______________________________

As you read *Kid Reporters at Work,* fill in the Venn Diagram.

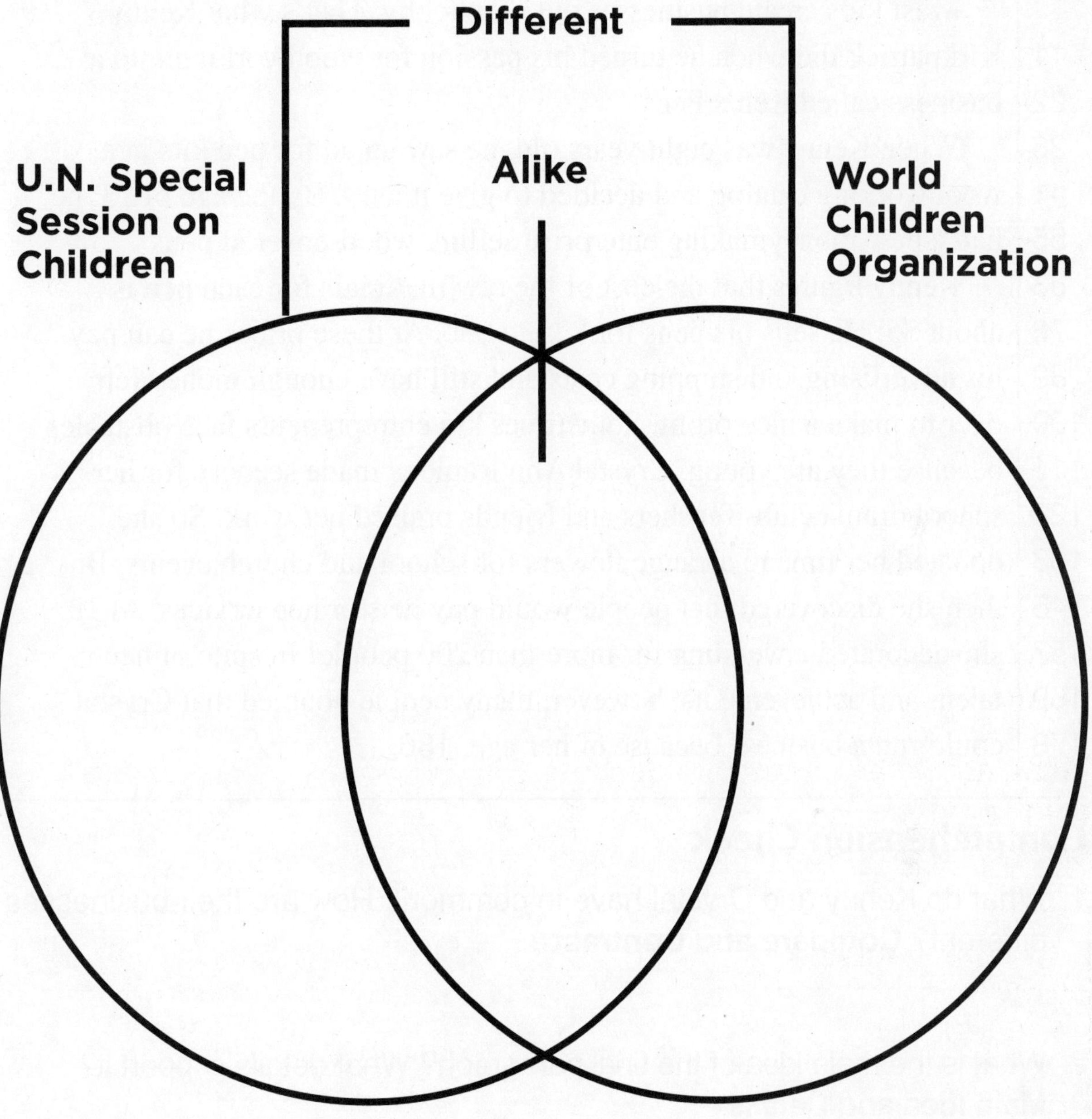

How does the information you wrote in the Venn diagram help you to summarize *Kid Reporters at Work*?

At Home: Have the student use the chart to retell the story.

Practice

Fluency

Name ________________________________

As I read, I will pay attention to tempo.

Most kids create businesses out of a hobby. That's what Kenny
11 Kirkpatrick did when he turned his passion for woodworking into a
22 business called Ken's Pens.
26 When Kenny was eight years old, he saw an ad for pen kits in a
41 woodworking catalog and decided to give it a try. By the age of 13, he
55 had a new moneymaking enterprise selling wood-covered pens.
63 Kenny figures that the cost of the raw materials for each pen is
76 about $5. He sells his pens for $25 to $50. At these prices he can pay
89 his advertising and shipping costs and still have enough money left
100 over to make a nice profit. Sometimes kid entrepreneurs face obstacles
111 because they are young. Crystal Ann Ramous made scenery for her
122 school drama club. Teachers and friends praised her work. So she
133 donated her time to arrange flowers for school and church events. But
145 then she discovered that people would pay her for her services. At 13,
157 she decorated a wedding for more than 200 people! In spite of her
169 talent and achievements, however, many people doubted that Crystal
178 could run a business because of her age. 186

Comprehension Check

1. What do Kenny and Crystal have in common? How are their businesses different? **Compare and Contrast**

2. What is the main idea of the final paragraph? What details support it? **Main Idea and Details**

	Words Read	–	Number of Errors	=	Words Correct Score
First Read		–		=	
Second Read		–		=	

At Home: Help the student read the passage, paying attention to the goal at the top of the page.

Name ______________________________

Imagine that you're working at the library, and it's your job to handle the card-catalog entries for the new books.

Create a card-catalog entry in the space below. It could be for one of your favorite books or for a book that you make up. Remember the following points as you create your entry:

- The publisher line describes where and when the book was published.
- The description tells how many pages the book has and whether it includes illustrations.
- A book can be listed under more than one subject.

Author

____

Title

____

Publisher

____

Description

____

Summary

____

____

Subject

____

____

At Home: Ask the student to explain the information shown in his or her card catalog entry to you.

Practice

Name ____________________

Vocabulary Strategy: Inflected Verb Endings

carry + ed or -ing	arrange + ed or -ing	ship + ed or -ing
decide + ed or -ing	reply + ed or -ing	answer + ed or -ing
enjoy + ed or -ing	hope + ed or -ing	hurry + ed or -ing
wonder + ed or -ing	try + ed or -ing	close + ed or -ing

You know the rules for adding *-ed* and *-ing* to verbs. Now put them to use. Write a story about friends who start a business together. Include the correct final spelling for at least ten of the words above.

____

____

____

____

____

____

____

____

____

____

____

____

____

____

At Home: Ask the student to read you his or her story. Have him or her identify the words chosen from the box and explain the final spellings.

Name ______________________________

- If ***c*** and ***g*** are followed by ***e, i,*** or ***y,*** they usually have a soft sound.
- If ***c*** and ***g*** are followed by ***a, o, u*** or any consonant except ***y,*** they usually have a hard sound.

List words with soft *c* and soft *g* under the appropriate heading.

Soft sound	**Hard sound**
______________	______________
______________	______________
______________	______________
______________	______________
______________	______________

Write a short rhymed or unrhymed poem, using the sounds of soft *c* and soft *g*.

____

____

____

____

____

____

____

At Home: Have the student recite his or her poem for you.

Name ____________________

patchwork	mysterious	responsibility	midst
loosened	amazement	sores	

Use the vocabulary words in the box to create a short story about life on the Great Plains. Write your story on the lines below. Be sure to use each word.

Name ______________________________

A logical **sequence of events** is one of the keys to writing a story that makes sense.

But who says that all stories have to be that way? On the lines below, write your own out-of-order story. Then try numbering the events in such a way that they do make sense.

_____ **1.** ______________________________

____

_____ **2.** ______________________________

____

_____ **3.** ______________________________

____

_____ **4.** ______________________________

____

_____ **5.** ______________________________

____

____

_____ **6.** ______________________________

____

At Home: Cut out four pictures from a magazine. Have your child use them to make up a story with a beginning, middle, and end.

Name ______________________________

Practice

Comprehension: Sequence

As you read *Mystic Horse,* fill in the Sequence Chart.

Event

↓

↓

↓

↓

↓

How does the information you wrote in the Sequence Chart help you to summarize *Mystic Horse*?

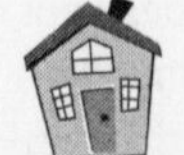

At Home: Have the student use the chart to retell the story.

Name ______________________________

As I read, I will pay attention to the tempo and try to match the energy and enthusiasm of the passage.

The Navajo are the largest tribe of Native Americans in North
11 America. The ancestors of the Navajo lived in northwestern Canada
21 and Alaska. More than 1,000 years ago, the Navajo began moving
32 south. They settled in the southwestern part of the United States where
44 the present-day states of Colorado, Utah, New Mexico, and Arizona
55 meet. The land is made up of plains, wind-swept cliffs, and high
68 mountains.

69 Spider Rock, the world's tallest natural spire, is located here in
80 Canyon de Chelly (da SHAY) National Park in Arizona. This amazing
89 red sandstone spire, which soars over 800 feet high, has an important
101 place in Navajo mythology. It is the home of Spider Woman, the
113 Navajo "fairy godmother."

116 The Navajo lived in homes called hogans. These houses were made
127 of wooden poles, mud, and tree bark. The Navajos also lived in caves
140 they built in the cliff walls of canyons. These caves were usually high
153 enough over the floor of the canyon so that the people would be safe
167 from enemies and dangerous floods. 172

Comprehension Check

1. Why might you think that Spider Woman is considered a kind and helpful mythological character? **Make Inferences**

2. What is the author's purpose in writing this selection? **Author's Purpose**

	Words Read	–	Number of Errors	=	Words Correct Score
First Read		–		=	
Second Read		–		=	

At Home: Help your child read the passage, paying attention to the goal at the top of the page.

Name ______________________________

Suppose you decided to create your own website. What subjects would you want to cover? What kinds of articles or stories would you include in it? How would you link them together? What would you call it?

In the space below, write a paragraph about a subject you know well. It could be your hobby, something you learned in school, or just about anything. Underline at least three words or phrases that would be *links* to other pages on your website. Make your page look as much like a web page as you can: Give the paragraph a title, a link to the "next" page at the end, and other features that you would like to have.

ADDRESS: ______________________ ⇨ GO

Search: type words GO

At Home: Have your child explain what is on the page each link goes to.

Name ______________________________

For each homophone pair below, write a sentence that includes both words.

1. soars/sores

____

____

2. horse/hoarse

____

____

3. write/right

____

____

4. prince/prints

____

____

5. heard/herd

____

____

6. whale/wail

____

____

At Home: Play a homophone game with your child. Say a homophone aloud and have your child tell you both spellings for it. Then trade roles.

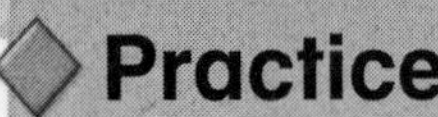

Name ________________________________

Find ten singular words in your classroom and list them in the left column. Then write the plural form of each word in the right column.

	Singular	Plural
1.	____________	____________
2.	____________	____________
3.	____________	____________
4.	____________	____________
5.	____________	____________
6.	____________	____________
7.	____________	____________
8.	____________	____________
9.	____________	____________
10.	____________	____________

At Home: Have your child explain the rules he or she used to form each plural.

Name ______________________________

technique	foolishness	inspire	evaporate
microscope	magnify	negatives	blizzard

Use the vocabulary words above to write a dialogue between two people stuck out in a snowstorm. Be sure to use each word at least once.

Name ______________________________

Read the selection. Then write a summary on the lines below.

Are you interested in weather? Maybe being a meteorologist is the career for you. A good background in math and science is important for this career. In addition, it's helpful to have a good understanding of computers and be a good communicator. And, of course, you should pay close attention to the weather.

You are probably familiar with the meteorologists on TV. They do just one of the jobs open to people who study weather. TV meteorologists forecast the weather. This means that they predict what the weather will be like in the days to come.

Other meteorologists are researchers. They study weather data. Some study it just to understand more about our planet's weather. Others do applied research; that is, they study weather to help weather predicting become more accurate.

Meteorologists can also be teachers or consultants. They use their knowledge to teach others about the weather or to provide information that might help a business or agency make informed decisions.

So if tracking a blizzard or studying how clouds move fascinates you, think about becoming a meteorologist!

____

____

____

____

____

____

____

At Home: Have the student find an article about the weather in a newspaper or magazine and summarize it for you.

Name ____

As you read *Snowflake Bentley,* fill in the Main Idea Web.

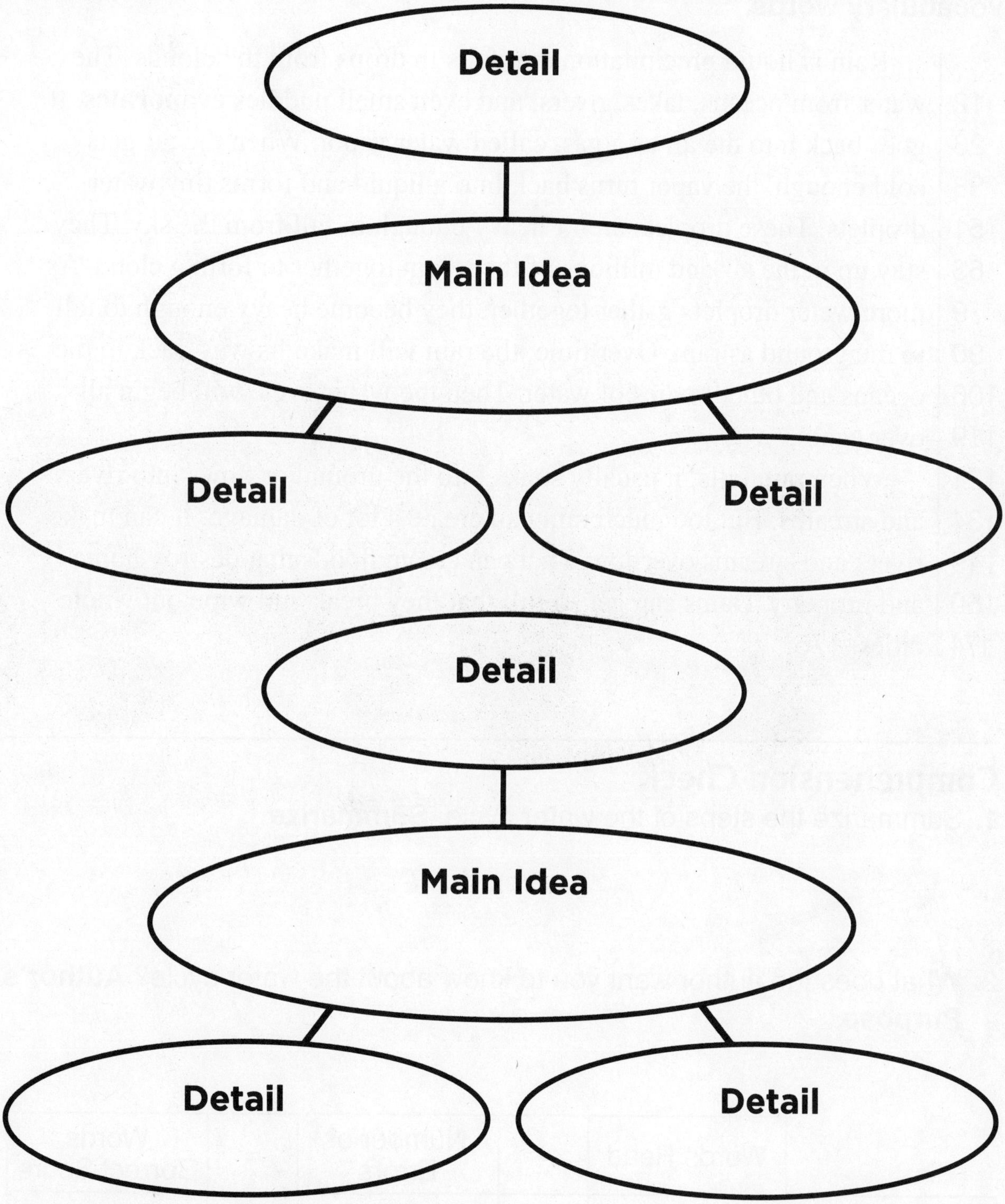

Detail

Main Idea

Detail

Detail

Detail

Main Idea

Detail

Detail

How does the information you wrote in the Main Idea Web help you evaluate *Snowflake Bentley*?

At Home: Have the student use the chart to retell the story.

Name ______________________________

As I read, I will pay attention to the pronunciation of vocabulary words.

Rain is liquid precipitation that falls in drops from the clouds. The
12 water from oceans, lakes, rivers, and even small puddles **evaporates**. It
23 goes back into the air as a gas, called water vapor. When the air gets
38 cold enough, the vapor turns back into a liquid and forms tiny water
51 droplets. These droplets aren't heavy enough to fall from the sky. They
63 stay up in the air and millions of them join together to form a cloud. As
79 more water droplets gather together, they become heavy enough to fall
90 to the ground as rain. Over time, the rain will make its way back to the
106 oceans and other bodies of water. Then the water cycle will begin all
119 over again.

121 When rain falls, it usually soaks into the ground or flows into rivers
134 and streams. But too much rain can create a lot of damage. It can make
149 rivers and streams overflow. That can create floods that destroy homes
160 and property. Dams can get so full that they break and wipe out whole
174 cities. 175

Comprehension Check

1. Summarize the steps of the water cycle. **Summarize**

2. What does the author want you to know about the water cycle? **Author's Purpose**

	Words Read	–	Number of Errors	=	Words Correct Score
First Read		–		=	
Second Read		–		=	

At Home: Help the student read the passage, paying attention to the goal at the top of the page.

Literary Elements: Imagery and Figurative Language

Name ______________________________

Complete the haikus with vivid imagry and figurative language.

1. The rain never stopped

____

____

2. Snow fell silently

____

____

3. The dark stormy night

____

____

4. The hail stones hammered

____

____

5. The sound of the wind

____

____

6. Ooooh--jalapeño.

____

____

7. Sheets on the clothesline

____

____

8. Not the alarm clock

____

____

9. Tomorrow's a dream

____

____

10. One little teardrop

____

____

11. Deep, deep in my heart

____

____

12. Like the cry of wolves

____

____

At Home: Talk with the student about the figurative language and imagery that he or she used above.

Practice

Vocabulary Strategy: Multiple-Meaning Words

Name ____________________

The words below have more than one meaning. Write two sentences for each word. Each sentence should use a different meaning of the word. Use a dictionary to check the meanings of words that you are unsure of.

1. fire

____

____

2. pack

____

____

3. cabinet

____

____

4. degree

____

____

5. object

____

____

6. post

____

____

Circle the word whose pronunciation changes depending on which meaning is intended.

At Home: Have the student find a multiple-meaning word in the dictionary. Challenge him or her to use the word twice in a sentence, using two different meanings.

Name ______________________________

A **compound word** is a word made by combining two other words. The new word has a meaning that is usually related to the meanings of the original words.

camp: an outdoor place to sleep and eat

fire: wood or another material that burns and gives off heat and light

campfire: a fire in a camp used for cooking or warmth

Write as many compound words as you can using the words in the box. You may use words more than once.

ball	fall	set	sun
beam	flake	shine	rise
burst	light	snow	thunder
drop	rain	storm	water

______________ ______________ ______________

______________ ______________ ______________

______________ ______________ ______________

______________ ______________ ______________

______________ ______________ ______________

______________ ______________ ______________

______________ ______________ ______________

______________ ______________ ______________

At Home: Think of a compound word. Give the student clues and see if he or she can guess the word. Then switch roles.

Name ______________________________

technique	negatives	patchwork	blizzard
magnify	mysterious	amazement	venture
guardian	tottered	agile	enterprising

Choose 10 vocabulary words from the box above. Write a sentence for each word, leaving a blank space where the vocabulary word should be. Exchange your sentences with a partner. Fill in the blanks in each other's sentences.

1. ______________________________
2. ______________________________
3. ______________________________
4. ______________________________
5. ______________________________
6. ______________________________
7. ______________________________
8. ______________________________
9. ______________________________
10. ______________________________

Name ______________________________

Draw pictures to represent six words from the box. Exchange pictures with a classmate. Try to identify the word represented by each picture.

proclaimed	unfair	ancestors	segregation
injustice	persistence	responsibility	inspire
foolishness	patchwork	numerous	avoided

Name ________________________________

risks	desperate	obedience	appreciated
bluffing	neglected	endured	misunderstood

Complete each sentence with a phrase that means the opposite of the underlined words in the sentence. For example, if the sentence begins, "He said he spoke the truth," you might complete the sentence "but I knew he was bluffing."

1. I was <u>hopeful</u> that I could find a new dog, ______________________
____

2. My dog was so full of <u>wild energy</u> that ______________________
____

3. The stray dog had once been <u>taken care of</u> ______________________
____

4. He said the plans were <u>totally safe</u> ______________________
____

5. When I gave him some water, the stray dog <u>complained</u> ____________
____

6. He <u>couldn't stand</u> my cat ______________________
____

Name ______________________________

Readers can often **draw conclusions** about characters and events based on what is said in the story and the readers' own experiences.

Read the story below and then write at least two conclusions that you can draw about the dog. Explain what you read that helped you draw each conclusion.

I called Wiggles, and she came running. When she saw the leash in my hand, she started to run around me in circles and bark. So I said, "Wiggles! Sit!" and she sat still while I got the leash on her.

Then we set off. Wiggles tugged at the leash and sniffed at everything we passed. When I called, "Heel!" she would drop back to walk beside me. Pretty soon, though, she would see something new and head straight for it, pulling me along.

When we got to the park I let her off the leash and we played "fetch" for a little while. She did a great job bringing the ball back. Usually, she would catch up to it before it stopped bouncing. But when I said, "Drop it!" she sometimes held onto the ball.

Just before it was time to go home, Wiggles saw a squirrel and dashed off across the meadow. The squirrel got safely up into a tree. Wiggles tried to climb straight up the trunk. When she couldn't, she just ran around and around the tree, barking excitedly. She didn't come when I called her. I had to go get her and put her leash on so that we could go home.

____

____

____

____

____

At Home: Read a newspaper article with the student and discuss the conclusions you can draw from it.

Name ______________________________

As you read *Dear Mrs. LaRue,* fill in the Conclusions Chart.

Text Clues	Conclusions

How does completing the Conclusions Chart help you to generate questions about *Dear Mrs. LaRue*?

At Home: Have the student use the chart to retell the story.

Name ______________________________

As I read, I will pay attention to punctuation.

Dogs and people go together. For thousands of years, they have
11 lived in each other's company.
16 Dogs helped hunters search for game and shepherds tend their
26 flocks. Dogs protected their human masters from danger and
35 unwelcome intruders.
37 Dogs are social animals too. They offer love and companionship
47 to the people around them.
52 Today most dogs live as pets. But some have jobs that require
64 special training. These dogs serve as helpers and companions to
74 people in need. They are well trained for the work they do.
86 Some helping dogs work in partnership with visually challenged
95 people. Others work with the hearing or physically challenged.
104 These dogs enable their human partners to live more independent lives.
115 Helping dogs also work in group facilities like nursing homes or
126 hospitals. These dogs provide welcome company for the many
135 residents or patients staying there.
140 Each type of helping work that a dog does demands certain skills.
152 It's often hard work for a dog to learn them. But for those dogs that
167 succeed, their benefit to humans is tremendous. Amazingly, all that
177 these dogs ask for in return is praise and loving care. 188

Comprehension Check

1. Why are dogs so easy to train? **Draw Conclusions**

2. Why did the author write this passage? **Author's Purpose**

	Words Read	–	Number of Errors	=	Words Correct Score
First Read		–		=	
Second Read		–		=	

At Home: Help the student read the passage, paying attention to the goal at the top of the page.

Name ____

Line graphs can show changes in all sorts of information over time: your allowance, your height, your bedtime—you name it. The graph below shows pet sales on the first five days of June.

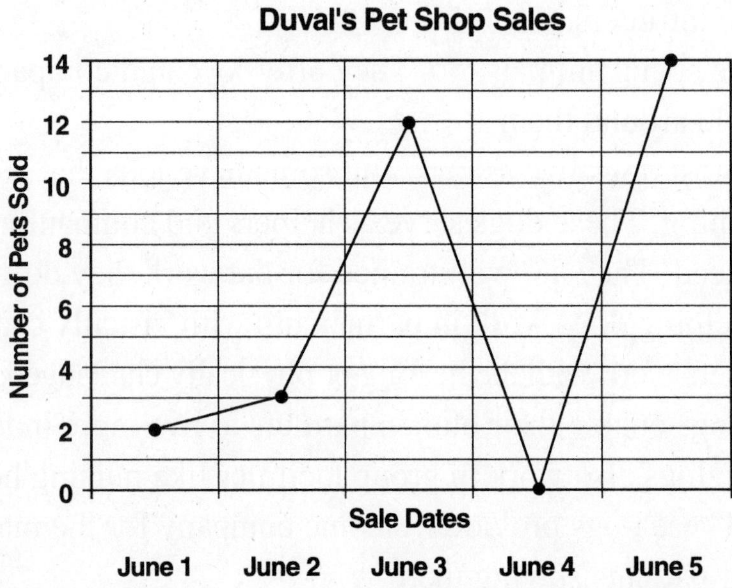

Write what the sales were for Duval's Pet Shop, and make up a story that could explain why more puppies were sold on some days and fewer on others.

____

____

____

____

____

____

____

At Home: Have the student keep a record for a week for a piece of information, such as the daily high temperature reported in the newspaper, and use it to make a line graph.

Name ______________________________

Add *mis-* to each word below. Then create a pet story using all of the words you have made. For example, you could write about a dog whose *misfortune* was due to his misbehavior. Use other *mis-* words if you want.

Words	**New Words**
1. behavior	____________
2. communication	____________
3. fortune	____________
4. pronounce	____________
5. inform	____________

Your Story

At Home: Have the student think of as many *mis-* words as he or she can in one minute.

Name ______________________________

How to make word equations with the endings *-ed* and *-ing:*
Add a letter if the word has a **short** vowel sound and ends in a consonant, like *rip.* Double the last letter before adding *-ed* or *-ing.*

rip + ing = ripping   rip + ed = ripped

Drop a letter if the word ends in *e.* Just drop the *e* before adding the ending.

save + ed = saved   save + ing = saving

Create your own word equations below. Write a one-syllable verb in the first blank, and either *-ed* or *-ing* in the second. Then write the completed word after the equal sign.

1. __________ + ______ = ______________
2. __________ + ______ = ______________
3. __________ + ______ = ______________
4. __________ + ______ = ______________
5. __________ + ______ = ______________
6. __________ + ______ = ______________
7. __________ + ______ = ______________
8. __________ + ______ = ______________
9. __________ + ______ = ______________
10. __________ + ______ = ______________

At Home: Ask the student to explain the spelling rules he or she used to create the *-ed* and *-ing* words above.

Name ______________________________

fade	cautiously	crisscrossed	wisdom
jealousy	disguised	faint	

Use the clues to fill in each vocabulary word in the crossword puzzle.

Down

2. dressed as someone else

3. grow dim

5. slight

Across

1. common sense

4. carefully

6. envy

7. marked by crossed lines

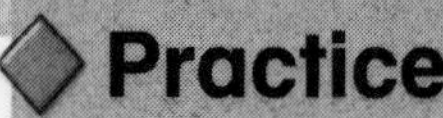

Name ____

When you **draw conclusions,** you use information from the story and your own experiences to decide something that is not directly stated in the story.

Read the passage below.

When Erik Weihenmayer was 13, he began to lose his sight, but he never lost his interest in mountain climbing. He followed sighted climbers as they went up a mountain. At the top, he listened to the wind in the trees, and felt the sun on his face. Commenting on his remarkable achievements Weihenmayer said, "There is a blurry line separating what the world sees as impossible, yet what we know in our hearts to be fully possible."

Draw a conclusion from the information in this passage and explain your reasoning.

1. ____

____

____

Now describe something that is not a reasonable conclusion to draw from the article. Why shouldn't people draw this conclusion?

2. ____

____

____

At Home: Have the student read a newspaper or magazine article and draw conclusions about the people described in the article.

Name ______________________________

As you read *The Blind Hunter,* fill in the Conclusions Chart.

Text Clues	Conclusions

How does completing the Conclusions Chart help you to generate questions about *The Blind Hunter*?

At Home: Have the student use the chart to retell the story.

Name ______________________________

As I read, I will pay attention to pauses, stops, and intonation.

During the 1940s and 1950s there was a serious outbreak of polio
10 in the United States. People were very frightened. Most of those who
22 got this disease were children. The most frightening thing about the
33 disease was that no one knew how it spread. People did not know how
47 to protect themselves or their children.
53 Scientists didn't know why, but polio seemed to spread faster during
64 the summer months. Many public swimming pools and beaches were
74 closed during this outbreak as a way to prevent the spread of polio.
87 Children were very cautious when they went outside because they
97 were afraid they would get sick. Polio is especially scary because a
109 small number of people who became ill were paralyzed for life. People
121 with paralysis cannot move their arms, legs, or other parts of the body.
134 Some people even died from polio.
140 Perhaps most of the fear came from the fact that not much was
153 known about polio. Even today, scientists don't know much more
163 about it than they did in the 1950s. 170

Comprehension Check

1. How did the fear of polio change children's lives in the 1950s? **Draw Conclusions**

2. How do you know that many polio survivors did not develop paralysis? **Make Inferences**

	Words Read	–	Number of Errors	=	Words Correct Score
First Read		–		=	
Second Read		–		=	

At Home: Help the student read the passage, paying attention to the goal at the top of the page.

Name ______________________________

Could you invent a device that would make life easier for people with physical challenges? Describe how people with disabilities would use your device.

____

____

____

____

____

Next create a glossary of two important words from the description of your device. Be sure to include the part of speech, pronunciation, syllable breakdown, and plural forms.

1. ______________________________

____

____

____

2. ______________________________

____

____

____

At Home: Have the student describe how the invention above works. Discuss the pros and cons of the invention.

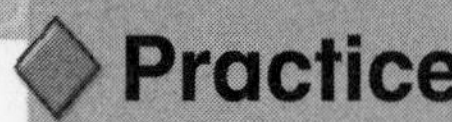

Name ______________________

Practice

Vocabulary Strategy: Word Families

Use wisdom, freedom, and kingdom in a story. Also include one other member of each word's family (for example, you could include *unwise* as a relation of *wisdom*). Write your story on the lines below.

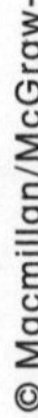

At Home: Pick one of the words above. Then ask the student to identify as many members of its word family as he or she can.

Name ______________________________

List five words ending with a consonant + *y* in the left blank under each heading below. Be sure that you can add the ending shown in the heading to the words you write under it. Then add the ending shown and write the correct spelling of each word in the right blank.

Add *-ed*	Add *-er*
1. ________ ________	11. ________ ________
2. ________ ________	12. ________ ________
3. ________ ________	13. ________ ________
4. ________ ________	14. ________ ________
5. ________ ________	15. ________ ________
Add *-es*	**Add *-est***
6. ________ ________	16. ________ ________
7. ________ ________	17. ________ ________
8. ________ ________	18. ________ ________
9. ________ ________	19. ________ ________
10. ________ ________	20. ________ ________

At Home: With the student, take turns identifying words that end in a consonant + *y* and spelling them with an *-ed*, *-est*, *-er*, or *-est* ending.

Name ______________________________________

globe	fuels	electrical	decayed

Use your book's glossary or a dictionary to find definitions for the vocabulary words and write them below, using your own words.

globe 1. ______________________________________

2. ______________________________________

fuels ______________________________________

____

electrical ______________________________________

____

decayed ______________________________________

____

Write two sentences using all of the vocabulary words.

____

____

____

____

Name ______________________________

Writers use the techniques of *persuasion* when trying to convince a reader to agree with them or to take a specific action. Write a letter to a friend asking him or her to take a specific action. For example, it might be for going to see a particular movie.

Be sure to include the following elements.

- a clear statement of what you want to do
  Let's go see Star Travelers *on Saturday at two o'clock at the Variety Cinema*.
- at least one fact in support of what you want to do
  Tickets there cost $2 less than they do at the Megaplex.
- at least one appeal to your friend's feelings
  It would be cool to be the first to see it.
- a strong concluding sentence
  So give me a phone call and tell me if you want to go.

____

____

____

____

____

____

____

____

At Home: Together, read a newspaper editorial and find the ways in which the writer tries to persuade readers.

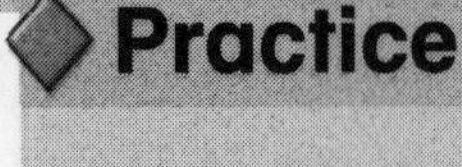

Name ___________________________

Comprehension: Make Inferences

As you read *The Power of Oil,* fill in the Inference/Opinion Web.

Clue

Clue

Inference

Clue

Clue

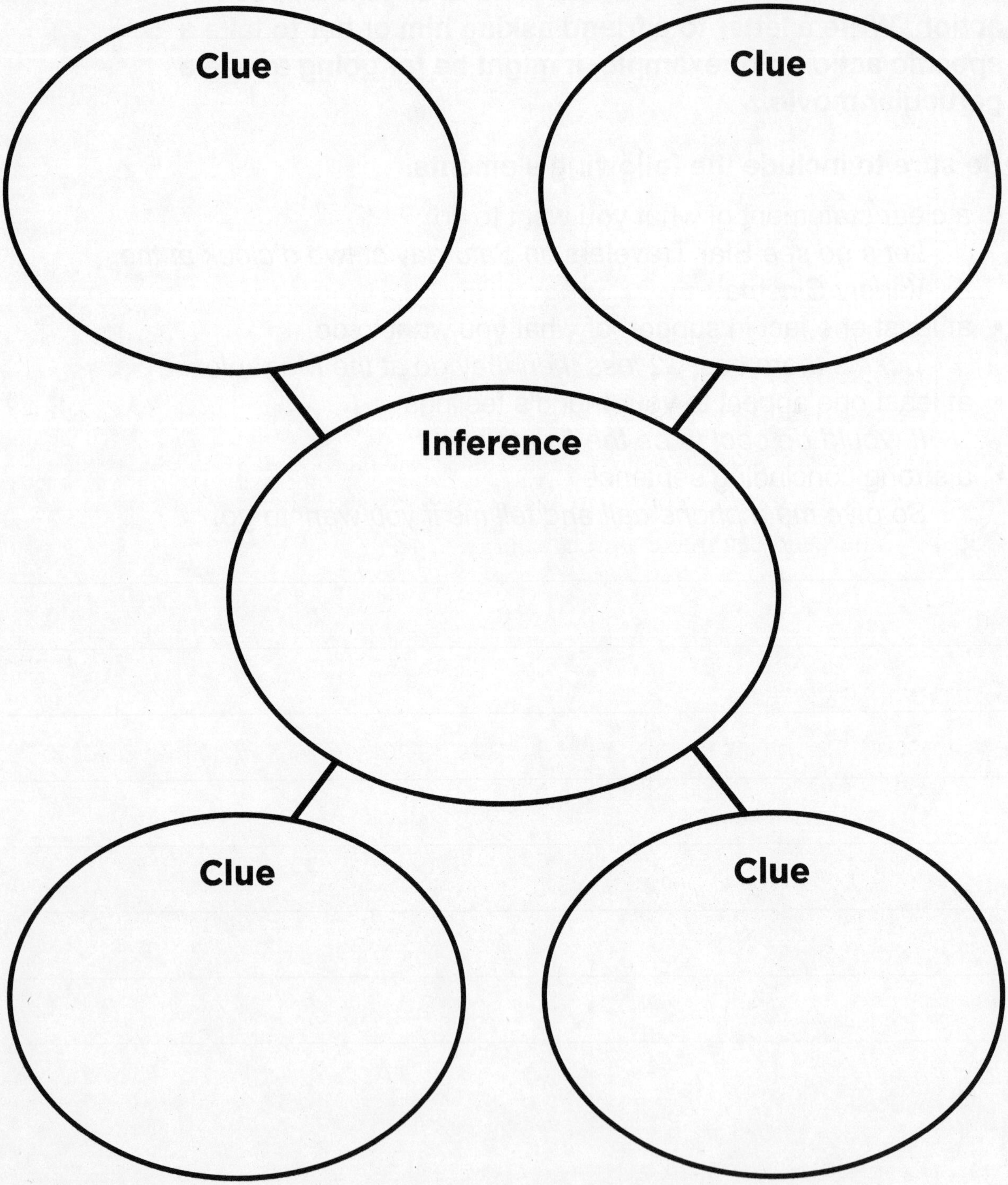

How does the information you wrote in the Inference/Opinion Web help you generate questions about *The Power of Oil*?

At Home: Have the student use the chart to retell the story.

Name ______________________________

As I read, I will pay attention to my pronunciation of vocabulary words and other difficult words.

What would happen if we didn't have electricity or gasoline? We
11 wouldn't be able to drive cars or ride trains. People living in cold areas
25 would have to burn wood to keep warm. And at night, everything
37 would be dark.
40 We get some of our electricity from the sun and from water. More
53 often we use **fuels**, such as petroleum and coal. These fuels were
65 formed millions of years ago from plants and animals that **decayed**.
76 The fuels cause air and water pollution. They are also nonrenewable
87 resources. That means they will run out someday.
95 Is it possible to find an energy source that won't run out and doesn't
109 pollute? It is! We already use solar panels and dams on rivers to make
123 electricity. But did you know that we can also use the wind?
135 The wind can make a lot of energy. 143

Comprehension Check

1. What technique does the author use to try to convince you that wind is a good energy source? **Persuasion**

2. How are petroleum and wind alike? How are they different? **Compare and Contrast**

	Words Read	–	Number of Errors	=	Words Correct Score
First Read		–		=	
Second Read		–		=	

At Home: Help the student read the passage, paying attention to the goal at the top of the page.

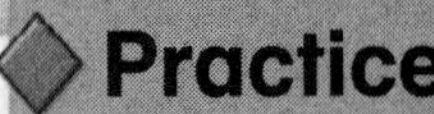

Practice

Study Skill: Media Center

Name ______________________________

Keywords are powerful tools when you're seeking information on the **Internet**. Picking the right set of words to use to conduct a search can bring the information you want to your fingertips. But keywords can be tricky, too. Sometimes one keyword can bring up two or more very different topics. For example, entering *solar* could give you Web pages on solar power and the solar system.

For each keyword below, write two different topics or search results that you get when you enter the word into a search engine by itself.

1. energy ______________________________

2. polar ______________________________

3. cook ______________________________

4. flight ______________________________

5. fossil ______________________________

6. Washington ______________________________

7. train ______________________________

8. oil ______________________________

At Home: Have the student explain how each keyword can bring up more than one topic. Discuss other keywords the student should use to limit his or her search.

Name ______________________________

Context clues can help readers determine the meaning of an unfamiliar word. Sometimes writers will provide the **definition** of a word in the context of a sentence or paragraph.

Read the words in the box. Then use each word in a short paragraph about energy. Provide a definition for each word as you use it.

electrical	decayed	globe	fuels

____

____

____

____

____

____

____

____

____

____

____

____

____

At Home: Have the student read a newspaper article. Whenever he or she encounters an unfamiliar word, have him or her use context clues to determine its meaning.

Use the clues to complete the crossword puzzle. Words with /ü/ sounds go across, and words with /u̇/ sounds go down. Words with /ū/ sounds do *not* go in the puzzle.

1. something to sit on

1. ought to

2. searching

2. not me, but __

3. the month after May

3. a chocolate-chip dessert

3. a box made of six squares

4. it's what comes from trees

4. it's what you eat

5. you make it with meat and potatoes

5. relative of a donkey

5. the opposite of sat

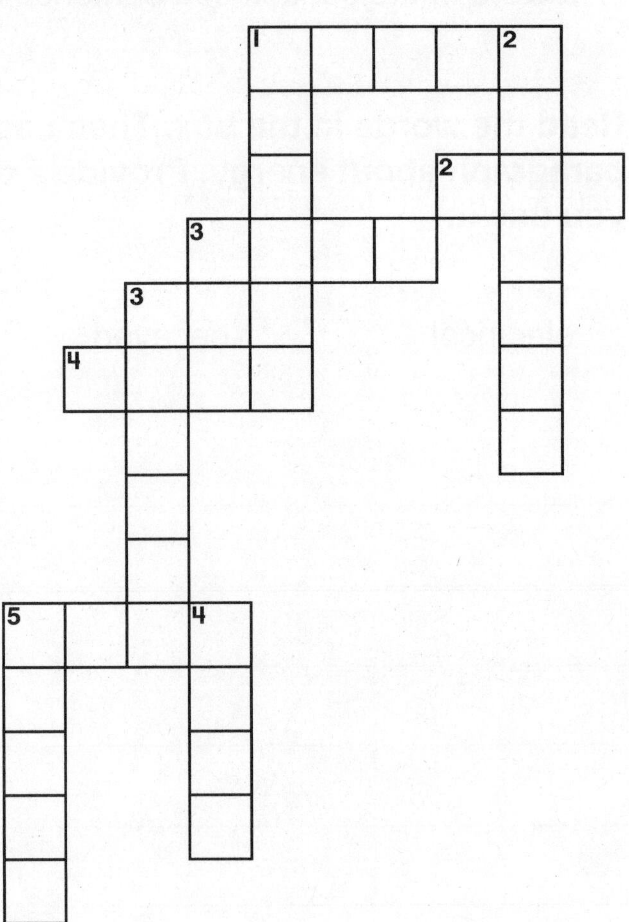

At Home: Have the student think of five other short /u̇/ and five other /ü/ words.

Name ____________________

dove	politicians	snoring	massive
tangles	rumbling	unique	

Use the vocabulary words to create a newspaper article about a pod of whales. Be sure to use all the words in the article. Write your article on the lines below.

Name ________________________________

Recall the sequence of events that happened on a vacation or during a special family event. Write down the sequence of events and put them in the correct order.

1. ____

____

2. ____

____

3. ____

____

4. ____

____

5. ____

____

6. ____

____

7. ____

____

8. ____

____

At Home: Have the student read a newspaper or magazine article. Then have him or her explain the sequence of events in the article.

Name ______________________________

As you read *Adelina's Whales,* fill in the Sequence Chart.

↓

↓

How does the information you wrote in the Sequence Chart help you to analyze the text structure of *Adelina's Whales*?

At Home: Have the student use the chart to retell the story.

Name ______________________________

As I read, I will pay attention to my tempo and try to match the action in the story.

It is a warm, sunny day. You are on a whale-watching boat trip.
13 Everyone is very excited. The captain promises that you will see a gray
26 whale. After just a little while, you realize this is going to be even
40 better than you thought. There is a mother gray whale and her calf
53 swimming near your boat.
57 You are admiring the baby whale, just the way the mother whale
69 seems to want you to. Suddenly a dark black fin appears in the water.
83 It's the dorsal fin of an orca whale. Now there are two dark black fins,
98 then three and four. What is happening? Six killer orca whales are
110 attacking the baby whale.
114 The mother does her best to fight them off. You keep watching,
126 hoping the mother can save her calf. She rolls like a log to push the
141 attackers away. Then she lifts the calf in the air with her flippers
154 so the baby is protected from the orca whales. Finally, the mother gray
167 whale manages to lead her calf to shallow waters. The killer whales do
180 not follow. 182

Comprehension Check

1. What events do the whale watchers witness from the boat? **Sequence**

2. Why do you think the orca whales attack the calf, but not the mother? **Draw Conclusions**

	Words Read	–	Number of Errors	=	Words Correct Score
First Read		–		=	
Second Read		–		=	

At Home: Help the student read the passage, paying attention to the goal at the top of the page.

Name ___________________________

Limericks may be short, but their format demands much thought to achieve the required meter and rhyme scheme. Study this limerick by Edward Lear. Then complete it by circling the correct words and explain whether each numbered word was chosen because of meter, rhyme scheme, or both.

There was an old man in a ______,
                                              1.
Whose whiskers were ______ to ______,
                                    2.   3.
But the birds of the ______
                               4.
Pluck'd them perfectly ______
                                   5.
To make themselves ______ in that tree.
                                  6.

1. tree   hickory

   Reason: ____________________

2. beautiful   lovely

   Reason: ____________________

3. see   witness

   Reason: ____________________

4. air   sea

   Reason: ____________________

5. clean   bare

   Reason: ____________________

6. comfortable   nests

   Reason: ____________________

Write your own limerick on the lines below. Be sure that your poem includes the correct rhyme scheme and meter.

____

____

____

____

____

At Home: Ask the student to read you his or her limerick and explain the meter and rhyme scheme.

Name ______________________________

Write three pairs of homographs and their meanings on the lines below.

1. ______________________________

____

2. ______________________________

____

3. ______________________________

____

Now write a short story using each of the homographs you wrote above.

____

____

____

____

____

____

____

____

____

____

____

At Home: Ask the student to explain the ways he or she used each homograph in the story.

Name ______________________________

Two different letter pairs stand for the **oi** sound.

oi **foil** oy **enjoy**

Two other letter pairs stand for the **ou** sound.

ou **couch** ow **frown**

Read the passage below. Circle the words that have the /oi/ sound. Underline the words that have the /ou/ sound.

A boy named Floyd found a mouse in the house. As he played with his toys, young Floyd enjoyed watching the mouse run around in the soil of the flower pots. Then the boy followed the mouse into the kitchen, where it carefully avoided Cook, carrying a bowl of boiling soup.

"Eeek!" shouted the boy's mother. "How did a mouse get into our lovely house?"

"I doubt whether we'll ever know how it got in, Mother. At the party last week it might have come in with the crowd on the hem of some proud lady's gown. Perhaps Cook brought it in full grown in a bag of flour. Maybe it was born in our barn and raised in our tower, and only now shows its little brown face without cowering. Oh, Mother, don't be a grouch! Don't pout and don't frown. Please don't shout or shoo it out. Our little friend makes no noise. It has no voice and will never be loud. How can you think of destroying what isn't annoying?"

"It's thoroughly spoiling an already rough day! I cannot allow it to stay in the house! Take your mouse outside now in an old, soiled pouch or I'll drown it or pound it or broil it today."

"Ouch," replied Floyd, and went in search of a pouch.

At Home: Spell out words that contain the letters *oi, oy, ou,* or *ow.* Ask the student to say the words aloud.

Name ____________________

coral	reef	brittle	eventually
current	partnership	suburbs	

Make your own crossword puzzle using the vocabulary words above. Figure out which words will go across and which will go down. Be sure that the words in your puzzle cross in the right places. Then write clues. When you're done, exchange puzzles with a partner.

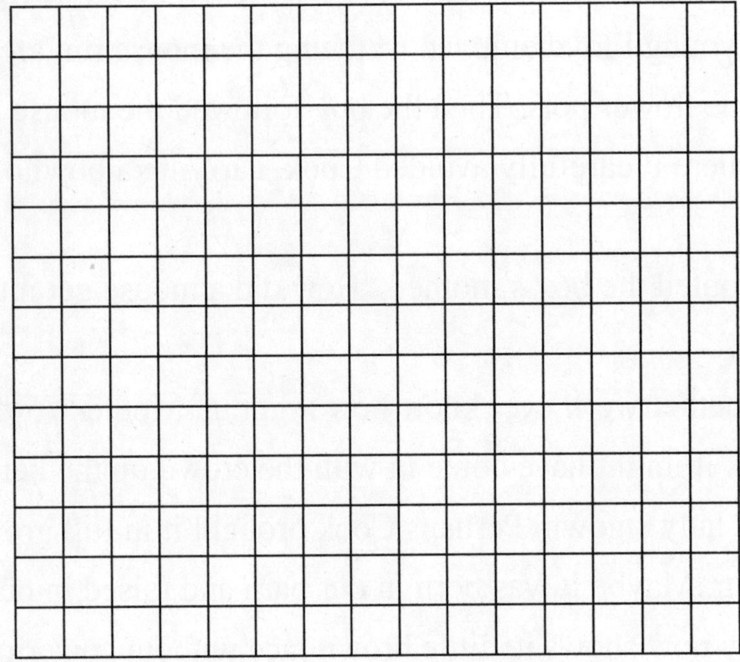

Across

____

____

____

____

Down

____

____

____

____

____

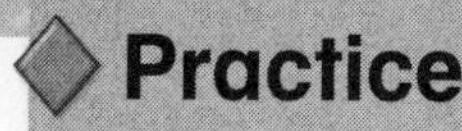

Name ______________________________

Comprehension: Compare and Contrast

Compare and contrast yourself with one of your friends or relatives. Write your name at the top of the first column. Complete the column by writing five things about yourself. Write the other person's name at the top of the second column. Then compare and contrast the other person with what you've written about yourself. If the two of you share the thing in common, write "same." If not, describe how the other person is different from you.

My Name: ______________	**His or Her Name:** ______________
1. ______________	**1.** ______________
______________	______________
2. ______________	**2.** ______________
______________	______________
3. ______________	**3.** ______________
______________	______________
4. ______________	**4.** ______________
______________	______________
5. ______________	**5.** ______________
______________	______________

At Home: Have the student explain his or her Compare and Contrast table to you.

Name ______________________________

As you read *At Home in the Coral Reef,* fill in the Venn Diagram.

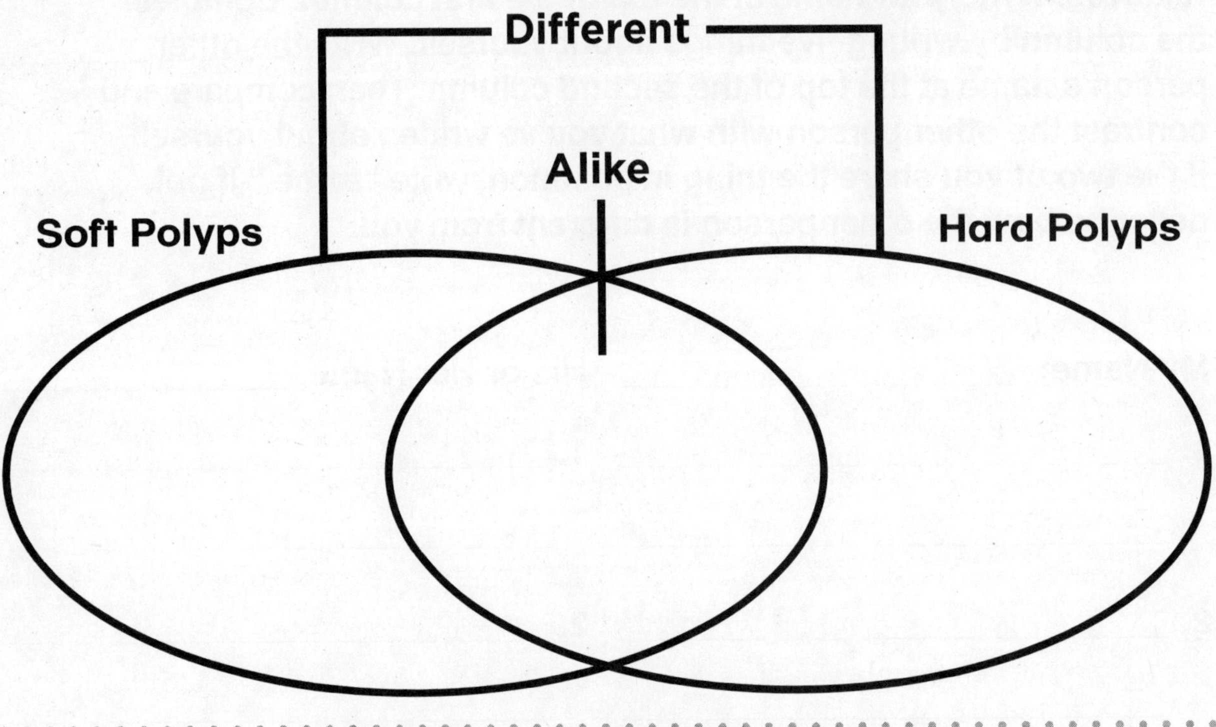

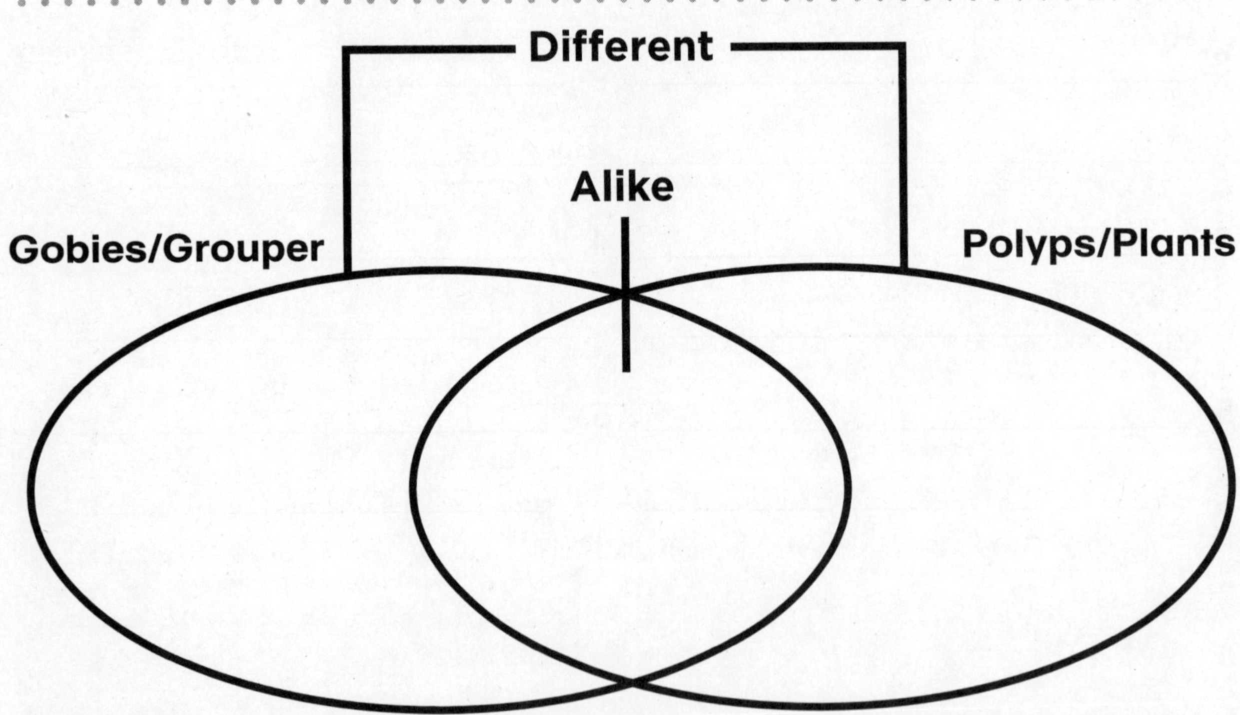

How does completing the Venn Diagram help you to analyze the text structure of *At Home in the Coral Reef*?

At Home: Have the student use the chart to retell the story.

Name ______________________________

As I read, I will pay attention to my pronunciation of vocabulary words.

Some ocean ecosystems are filled with bizarre and beautiful life forms.
11 In warm, shallow waters, lush **coral** reefs bustle with life. Tourists visit
23 these reefs to see thousands of colorful fish.
31 In other ocean ecosystems, life struggles to survive in harsh conditions. Salt
43 water is poison to most trees. But mangrove trees manage to grow in the
57 ocean's salty water. These trees provide food and shelter to many small
69 animals.
70 There is another ecosystem where conditions are even harsher. It rivals
81 the coral reefs for bizarre and beautiful life forms.
90 It is a world of towering chimneys squirting out what looks like black
103 smoke. It is a world filled with creatures that look like puffy orange balls
117 and giant pens with bright red caps.
124 Scientists only discovered this fantastic world in the 1970s. It is the
135 world of hydrothermal vents.
139 Hydrothermal vents remained a secret for so long because they are hidden
151 at the bottom of the ocean. They lie under more than a mile of water and
167 it was not until the 1950s that submarines could dive down that deep. 179

Comprehension Check

1. How are coral reefs and hydrothermal vents similar? How are they different? **Compare and Contrast**

2. What conclusion can you draw about the amount of light around hydrothermal vents? **Draw Conclusions**

	Words Read	–	Number of Errors	=	Words Correct Score
First Read		–		=	
Second Read		–		=	

At Home: Help the student read the passage, paying attention to the goal at the top of the page.

Name ______________________________

A **protagonist** is a story's main character. **Hyperbole** is the use of exaggeration to make a point or create drama.

Write a story about a protagonist who uses hyperbole when he or she talks. Before you start writing, think about how other characters respond to these exaggerations. Are they confused or amused? Are they irritated or captivated?

____

____

____

____

____

____

____

____

____

____

____

____

____

____

____

At Home: Have the student read his or her story to you. Discuss examples of hyperbole in the story.

Name ______________________________

Sometimes writers will provide **descriptions** as context clues in order to help their readers clarify a word's meaning.

Supply descriptions as context clues for each of the following five words. Be sure that the descriptive context clues help make the meanings of the words clear.

harsh	sunken	gusts	compass	cargo

1. ______________________________
____

2. ______________________________
____

3. ______________________________
____

4. ______________________________
____
____

5. ______________________________
____

At Home: Have the student read a story and identify any unfamiliar words. Then have him or her use context clues to figure out the meaning of the words.

Name ________________________________

You can find the ***/ô/ sound*** in words like *caller, walker, shawl,* and *caught.*

List eight words with the /ô/ sound. Underline the letters that stand for the sound. Then write a sentence for each word.

1. ______________ ____________________________________

____

2. ______________ ____________________________________

____

3. ______________ ____________________________________

____

4. ______________ ____________________________________

____

5. ______________ ____________________________________

____

6. ______________ ____________________________________

____

7. ______________ ____________________________________

____

8. ______________ ____________________________________

____

At Home: Read a magazine or newspaper article with the student. List all the words with the /ô/ sound that you can find in the article.

Name ______________________________

Draw pictures to represent six words from the box. Exchange pictures with a classmate and try to identify the word represented by each picture.

disguised	fade	snoring	tangles	dove
partnership	suburbs	decayed	neglected	endured
obedience	cautiously	crisscrossed	electrical	rumbling

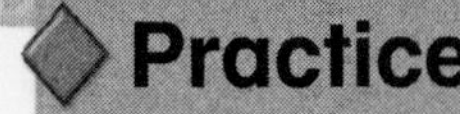

Name ______________________

Unit 4
Vocabulary Review

Write a story using six of the vocabulary words below. Choose the words you will use before starting to write. Continue your story on a separate sheet of paper, if necessary.

disguised	bluffing	massive	neglected
desperate	wisdom	rumbling	tourists
eventually	decayed	unique	tangles

Name ______________________________

snuffled	selecting	positive
consisted	peculiar	advanced

Write a story about a library visited by a large animal—a dog, a bear, or something else?—using all the vocabulary words above.

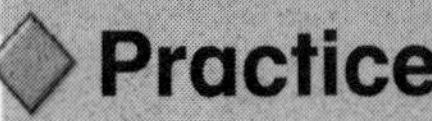

Name ____________________

Use your own words and include only the most important information in a **summary.**

Read the following passage. Then summarize it.

Chances are, your local public library has a Children's Room. This is a separate room within a library where kids can go to browse and read books written specifically for children. Sometimes, the children's room librarian will read aloud some children's books to the kids who are visiting.

Children's books have been included in public libraries since 1895. In 1899, special rooms for children began to be included in library designs as new libraries were built. These rooms were designed with children in mind. Smaller chairs and tables are often set up in this section of a library. You might also see a reading corner with big pillows on the floor. In 1901, the Andrew Carnegie Free Library in Carnegie, Pennsylvania, designed a children's room with low bookcases so children could reach the books.

The idea of a Children's Library Story Time began in 1899. Charlotte Keith was the first Children's Librarian in a library in Pittsburgh, Pennsylvania. She started a story time to attract young readers to the library. The tradition has continued to this day.

____

____

____

____

____

____

At Home: Together, read the student's summary above. Ask him or her to explain why some information was included in the summary and some wasn't.

Name ____

As you read *Because of Winn-Dixie,* fill in the Summarizing Chart.

How does the information you wrote in the Summarizing Chart help you to evaluate *Because of Winn-Dixie*?

At Home: Have the student use the chart to retell the story.

Name ______________________________

As I read, I will pay attention to end punctuation in each sentence.

Alicia pulled up the collar of her parka as a cold gust of
13 wind blew past. It wasn't hot, it wasn't sunny, and the beach
25 was 3,000 miles away in Florida, where they used to live before
36 Mom got a new job in Seattle. It had been a month since their
50 family had moved to Everton, a town outside Seattle, and Alicia
61 still wasn't used to the weather. In Miami it was usually in the
74 70s in February. But here every day seemed to be cold and wet.
86 The skies were gray, and the air had a peculiar smell. It was
99 nothing like the salty sea air she was used to.

109 Mark kicked a stone and watched it skip into a puddle. "Of
121 course," he thought to himself. "Where isn't there a puddle?"
131 He knew that was an exaggeration. It didn't always rain here. It
143 was just that when it rained in Florida, the skies cleared up
155 afterward. Here the skies stayed overcast for days. But Mark
165 tried to stay cheerful. He had read about the Pacific Northwest
176 and learned that the weather during the summer was just fine.
187 Then they would go to the mountains, which would be really
198 exciting. 199

Comprehension Check

1. Even though Seattle and Miami are near oceans, how do they differ? **Compare and Contrast**

2. How do the characters feel about their new home? **Draw Conclusions**

	Words Read	–	Number of Errors	=	Words Correct Score
First Read		–		=	
Second Read		–		=	

At Home: Help the student read the passage, paying attention to the goal at the top of the page.

Name ______________________

Onomatopoeia is the use of a word that imitates the sound that it stands for.
A **simile** compares two different things, usually by using the word *like, as,* or *than.*

Describe an exciting event using onomatopoeia. Try to use onomatopoeia at least two times.

____

____

____

____

____

Write three sentences, each using a simile to describe the way someone looks.

____

____

____

____

____

____

At Home: Together, read what the student wrote. Discuss the impact that each onomatopoeia and simile had.

Name ______________________________

Write a synonym for each of the words below. Choose a synonym with a different connotation. Use it in a sentence, and then explain how your new word is different.

1. A synonym for *full*: ______________

Sentence: ______________________________

How my word is different: ______________________________

____

2. A synonym for *small*: ______________

Sentence: ______________________________

How my word is different: ______________________________

____

3. A synonym for *sad*: ______________

Sentence: ______________________________

How my word is different: ______________________________

____

4. A synonym for *walk*: ______________

Sentence: ______________________________

How my word is different: ______________________________

____

At Home: Ask the student to think of a third synonym for each word above. Then discuss the connotation of the third word, and use it in a sentence.

On the lines below, list ten two-syllable words that have the VC/CV pattern. Write the first syllable in the left blank and the second syllable in the right blank.

	First Syllable	Second Syllable
1.	______	______
2.	______	______
3.	______	______
4.	______	______
5.	______	______
6.	______	______
7.	______	______
8.	______	______
9.	______	______
10.	______	______

On the lines below, write pairs of words. One word should have the VC/CV pattern, and the other should not. Have a partner circle the word with the VC/CV pattern in each pair.

11. ______ ______

12. ______ ______

13. ______ ______

14. ______ ______

At Home: Look through newspapers or books to identify ten more examples of VC/CV pattern words.

Name ______________________________

cranky	bumbling	selfish	exasperated
specialty	famished	commotion	

Imagine that you are writing a play. On the lines below, describe four of the characters in your play. Use all of the vocabulary words.

1. ______________________________

____

____

2. ______________________________

____

____

3. ______________________________

____

____

4. ______________________________

____

____

Name ____

When you read or watch a play, you **make judgments** about the characters based on what they say and do.

Read the passage below and then write down the judgments you made about the characters. Did your judgments change as you read? Explain.

Jarela: Cook, could I have some soup?

Cook: No, you can't. I'm busy with other things. You'll have to wait.

Jarela: But I'm so hungry. *Please* give me some soup.

Cook: I said no.

Jarela: What if I helped you with something first? What could I do?

Cook: Well, you could scrub out those pots.

Jarela scrubs out the pots.

Cook: Thank you. Here's some chicken noodle soup.

Jarela: Oh, my favorite! Thank you very much.

____

____

____

____

____

____

____

____

____

At Home: Together, read the dialogue the student wrote. Make judgments about the characters. Discuss how the dialogue helped you make your judgments.

Name ______________________________________

As you read *Ranita, the Frog Princess,* fill in the Make Judgments Flow Chart.

	→	
	→	
	→	
	→	
	→	
	→	

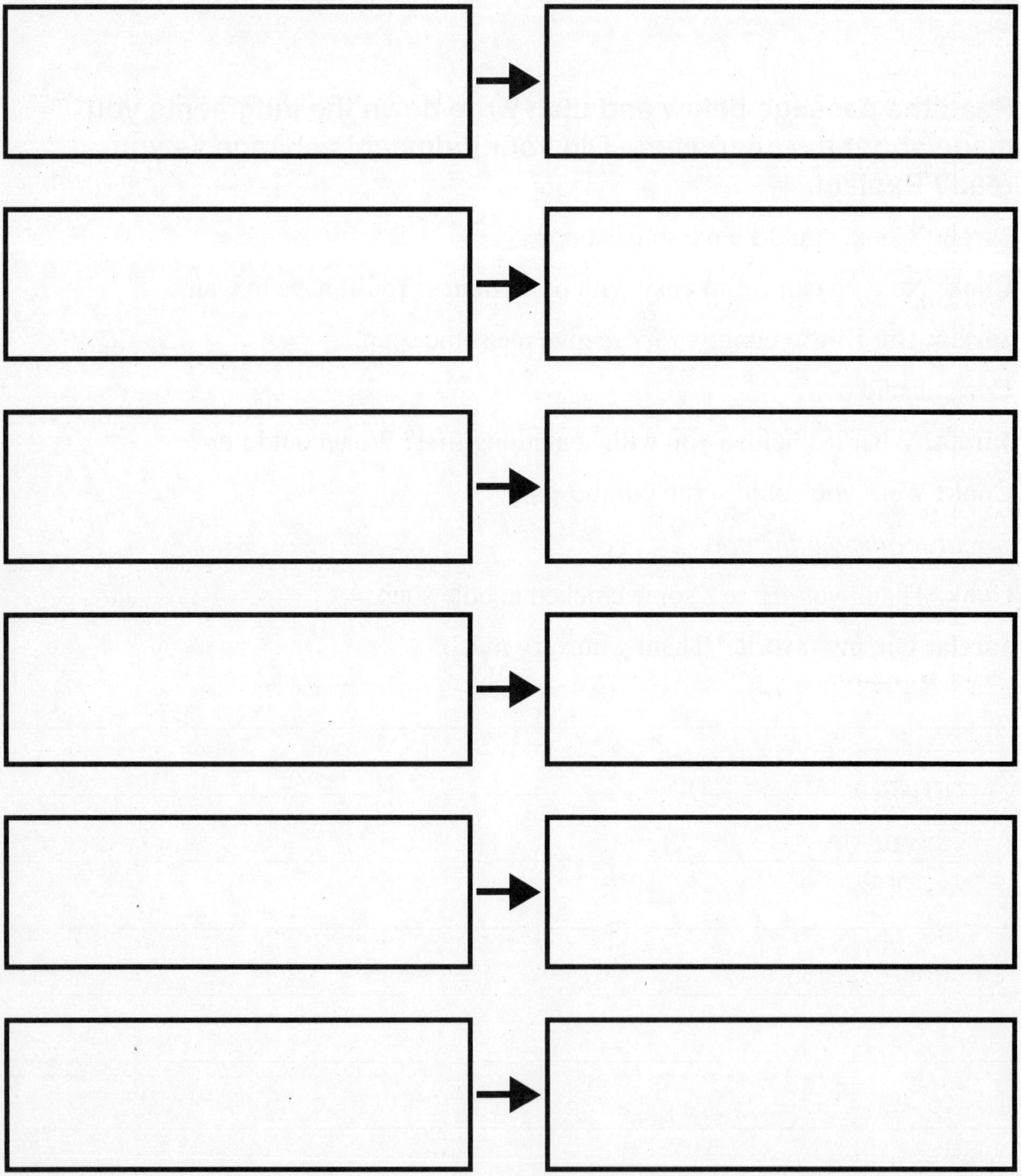

How does the information you wrote in the Make Judgments Flow Chart help you to evaluate *Ranita, the Frog Princess*?

At Home: Have the student use the chart to retell the story.

Name ______________________________

As I read, I will pay attention to dialogue and characters' roles.

[Enter Rafael and Pauline from opposite sides of the stage. Rafael is
12 *carrying a soccer ball under his arm and a math test in his hand.*
26 *Pauline is carrying an armful of books.]*
33 ***Rafael:*** *(smiling and waving a math test)* Hey, Pauline! I got an "A" on
47 my math test. Thanks for your help!
54 ***Pauline:*** *(peers over the top of the books she's holding)* Good job! And
67 guess what? I got an "A" on the French test.
77 ***Rafael:*** *(takes some of her books)* That's great! Why don't we
88 celebrate? We could go to the park and kick a soccer ball around.
101 ***Pauline:*** No thanks. I have rehearsal for *Sleeping Beauty* tonight and I
113 need to finish my homework. Why don't we just study?
123 ***Rafael:*** ***(exasperated)*** You know what? You still haven't learned how to
134 have any fun.
137 ***Pauline:*** Yeah? Well, you're just a silly boy. *[Rafael and Pauline glare*
149 *at one another. Enter a man in a suit holding a cell phone.]*
162 ***Man in Suit:*** *(to Rafael)* Excuse me, your highness. The king wishes to
175 speak to you.
178 ***Rafael:*** *(taking the cell phone and speaking into it)* Dad? 188

Comprehension Check

1. Did Pauline make the right decision to choose homework over relaxing? Why or why not? **Make Judgments**
2. What clues suggest that if Rafael and Pauline can stop arguing, they might make a good team? **Draw Conclusions**

	Words Read	–	Number of Errors	=	Words Correct Score
First Read		–		=	
Second Read		–		=	

At Home: Help the student read the passage, paying attention to the goal at the top of the page.

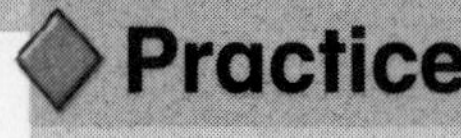

Text Feature: Interview

Name ____

Conduct your own interview with a partner from your class. On the lines below, write at least four questions for your partner to answer about his or her favorite actor. Then ask your partner the questions and record his or her answers on the lines below.

Q: ____

A: ____

____

____

Q: ____

A: ____

____

____

Q: ____

A: ____

____

____

Q: ____

A: ____

____

____

At Home: Have the student interview you about what it was like when you were growing up.

Name ______________________________

Write as many antonyms as you can for each word below.

1. hot

______________ ______________

______________ ______________

2. noisy

______________ ______________

______________ ______________

3. pleased

______________ ______________

______________ ______________

4. slow

______________ ______________

______________ ______________

5. funny

______________ ______________

______________ ______________

6. confused

______________ ______________

______________ ______________

At Home: Together, make up a story using words and their antonyms.

Name ____________________

If the first syllable of a word is **open,** the vowel sound is long, and the syllables break in the **V/CV pattern**.
If the first syllable of a word is **closed,** the vowel sound is short, and the syllables break in the **VC/V pattern**.

On the lines below, write ten words with an open first syllable and ten words with a closed first syllable. Divide the syllables with a slanted line (/).

Open First Syllable	Closed First Syllable
1. ____________	11. ____________
2. ____________	12. ____________
3. ____________	13. ____________
4. ____________	14. ____________
5. ____________	15. ____________
6. ____________	16. ____________
7. ____________	17. ____________
8. ____________	18. ____________
9. ____________	19. ____________
10. ____________	20. ____________

At Home: Together, divide the following words into syllables: *radar, cabin, stolen, diver, river.* Then compose a silly sentence that uses all the words.

Name ________________________

period vessels valuable documenting estimated

Write a short story about a crew of explorers on an ocean journey. They can be below the ocean's surface searching for anything you choose. Use each vocabulary word at least once.

Name ______________________________

Identify which of the following statements are facts and which are opinions.

1. The Spanish explorers were braver than the French or the Portuguese.

   ____

2. Columbus set out across the Atlantic Ocean in 1492.

   ____

3. In the 1500s the Spanish explored Mexico, Central America, and South America. ____________

4. Ponce de León explored Puerto Rico and Florida. ____________

5. Most people would agree that Hernán Cortés, who explored Mexico, is the best known of all explorers. ____________

6. The most important find occurred when Hernando de Soto discovered the Mississippi River. ____________

Rewrite four of the statements above, turning the facts into opinions and the opinions into facts.

7. ____

   ____

8. ____

   ____

9. ____

   ____

10. ____

    ____

At Home: Take turns making statements about your neighborhood and deciding whether each statement is a fact or an opinion.

Name ______________________________

As you read *Exploring the Undersea Territory*, fill in the Fact and Opinion Chart.

Facts	Opinions

How does the information you wrote in the Fact and Opinion Chart help you to evaluate *Exploring the Undersea Territory*?

At Home: Have the student use the chart to retell the story.

Name ______________________________

As I read, I will pay attention to my pronunciation of vocabulary and other difficult words.

Marco Polo was born around 1254 in Venice, Italy. His father and
11 uncles were successful merchants. When Marco was born, his father,
21 Niccolo, and his uncle, Maffeo, were in Constantinople. The Polos left
32 Constantinople in about 1260. They set out eastward, along the Black
42 Sea. Marco did not meet his father until years later.
52 In this **period** the Mongol Empire ruled much of Asia. Local
63 Mongol leaders, or khans, ruled different regions. The greatest was
73 Kublai Khan, the ruler of Cathay. That was what medieval Europeans
84 called China. After four years of travel, the Polos reached the Great
96 Khan's court. He was probably at his summer palace. It was called
108 Shang-du, or Xanadu (ZAN-ah-doo).
112 The Polos won Kublai Khan's favor. After a while, he sent them back
125 home to Europe. Their trip paved the way for Marco's own adventures.
137 The Polos could not stay home for long since Kublai Khan was
149 expecting them back. Marco's father and uncle left again after being
160 home for only two years. This time, the teenaged Marco went with
172 them. They traveled by camel across what is now Turkey and
183 northern Iran. 185

Comprehension Check

1. Why do you think trading trips took years? **Draw Conclusions**

2. What kinds of characteristics did the Polos have? **Character**

	Words Read	–	Number of Errors	=	Words Correct Score
First Read		–		=	
Second Read		–		=	

At Home: Help the student read the passage, paying attention to the goal at the top of the page.

Name ______________________________

Skim the following passages and write the name of the report you could use the information for.

The best time for birding on the island is from August to November. The Ranomafana rainforest is home to the crested ibis and the red-tailed vanga, while Zombitse National Park is the best place for locating the stately giant coua and the impressive Madagascar hoopoe.

1. ______________________________

____

Treatment begins with removing the victim from the water and performing CPR to bring oxygen to the lungs, heart, and brain. CPR, which should be attempted only by people who have been trained and certified in its use, consists of the following sequence of steps.

2. ______________________________

____

In 1500 Vasco Núñez de Balboa sailed with Rodrigo de Bastidas from Spain to Colombia, and they set out to search for treasures along the northern coast of South America. In 1511 Balboa founded the first European settlement in South America, and in 1513 he discovered the Pacific Ocean.

3. ______________________________

____

Born in Gibbstown, New Jersey, Sylvia Earle was raised on a small farm near Camden. From the time she was small, Sylvia was fascinated by the creatures and plants she found as she explored the woods near her home. Then when Sylvia was 13, her family moved to Clearwater, Florida.

4. ______________________________

____

5. Once you realized that a book would be useful in writing your report, you would use the Index or Table of Contents to find out which pages might have the information you needed. To locate a certain date or place name on one of these pages, what would you do?

____

At Home: Discuss with the student when it is better to skim a passage and when it is better to scan.

Name ______________________________

An **analogy** is a comparison between two pairs of words that have the same relationship.

Determine the relationship between the words. Then complete the analogies.

1. *Wonderful* is to *fabulous* as *terrifying* is to ______________.
2. *A* is to ______________ as *one* is to *number*.
3. *Lion* is to *roar* as ______________ is to *hiss*.
4. ______________ is to *jacket* as *zipper* is to *trousers*.
5. *Cloud* is to *sky* as *wave* is to ___________.
6. *Marshmallow* is to ___________ as *lemon* is to *iced tea*.
7. *First* is to *last* as *George Washington* is to ______________.
8. ___________ is to *dentist* as *eye* is to *optometrist*.
9. *Glove* is to ___________ as *sock* is to *foot*.
10. ___________ is to *Massachusetts* as *Cape May* is to *New Jersey*.
11. *Gills* are to *fish* as ___________ are to *humans*.

Now it is your turn to create analogies. Fill in three blanks in each sentence. Then swap with a partner to complete the fourth.

12. ___________ is to ___________ as ___________ is to ___________.
13. ___________ is to ___________ as ___________ is to ___________.
14. ___________ is to ___________ as ___________ is to ___________

At Home: Discuss the analogies the student wrote above.

Name ___________________________

List six two-syllable words that have an accented first syllable. Then list six two-syllable words with an accented final syllable.

Accented First Syllable	**Accented Second Syllable**
1. ______________	7. ______________
2. ______________	8. ______________
3. ______________	9. ______________
4. ______________	10. ______________
5. ______________	11. ______________
6. ______________	12. ______________

Write a long sentence or two smaller sentences containing mostly two-syllable words, all accented on the first syllable. Make sure that everything you write is about the same subject. For fun, see if you can get some neighboring words to begin with the same letter of the alphabet. Can you manage to have the last word of the second sentence rhyme with the last word in the first sentence, or with a word somewhere in the middle?

13. ____

____

14. ____

____

What have you created? ______________

At Home: Set a timer for one minute and identify as many items as you can with the accent on the first syllable. Do the same for items with the accent on the second syllable.

Name ____________________

strutting	swarms	flicked	barbecue
skyscrapers	glorious	collage	

Suppose you went to a museum on a class trip. On the lines below, write a journal entry to describe the different pieces of artwork that you saw. Use each vocabulary word at least once.

Name ____

curious	impatient	artistic	lazy	friendly

Choose one of the words in the box. Write a passage about a character who could be described using the word you chose. But don't include the word in your passage! Instead, include examples of how your character might act and what he or she might say and feel. When you finish, exchange passages with a classmate. Did your classmate guess the right word?

____

____

____

____

____

____

____

____

____

____

____

____

____

____

At Home: Together, read the passage the student wrote. Discuss how the reader can tell what the character is like based on the description.

Name ________________________________

As you read *Me and Uncle Romie,* fill in the Character Web.

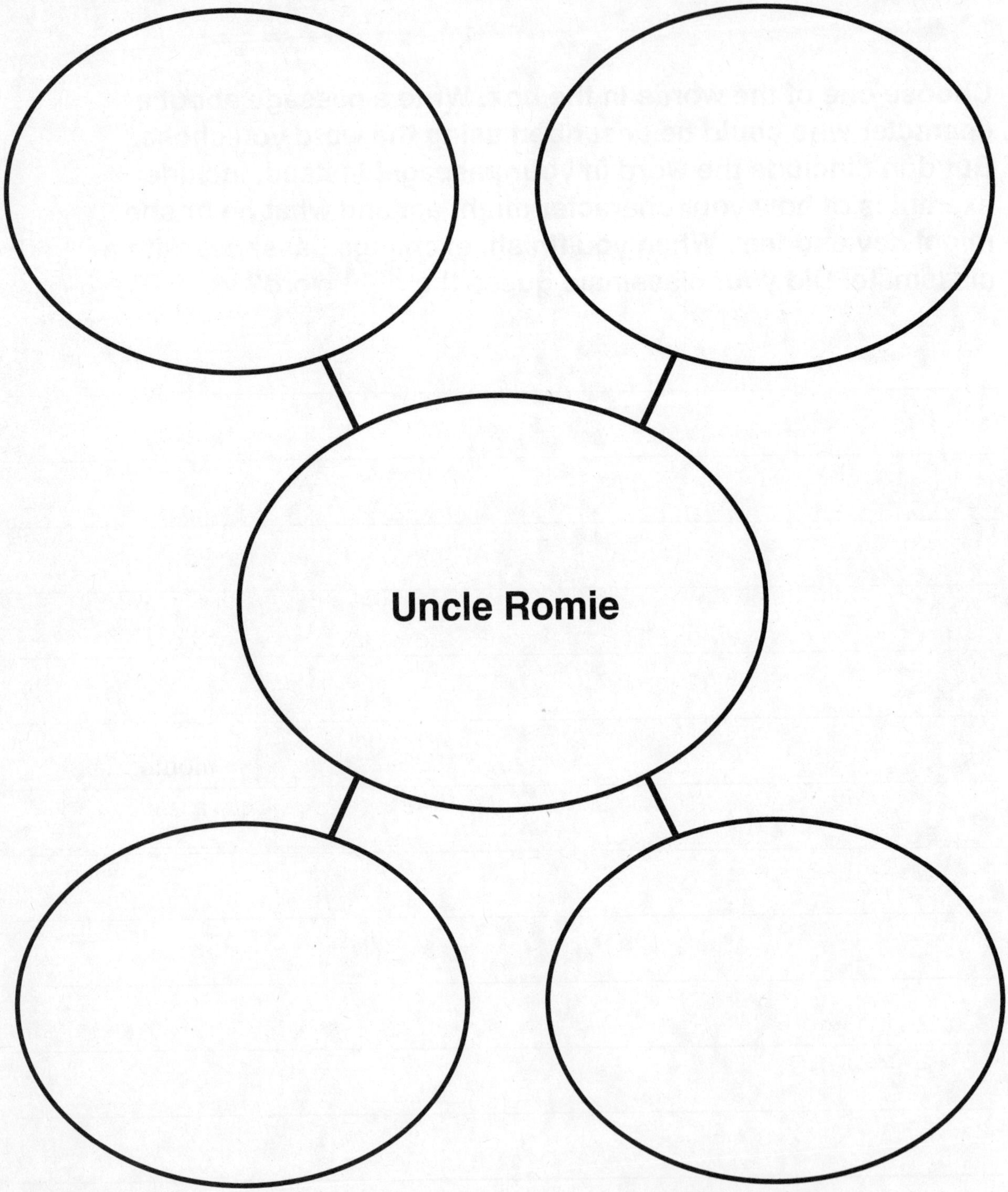

Uncle Romie

How does the information you wrote in the Character Web help you to monitor your comprehension of *Me and Uncle Romie*?

At Home: Have the student use the chart to retell the story.

Name ______________________________

As I read, I will pay attention to my tempo in order to match the action in the story.

"Over here, over here!"
4 I followed the voice and found Benvenuto lurking around the
14 corner of Signor Agnolo's shop.
19 "Hold on," he said. "I'll go with you on your errand."
30 "Aren't you supposed to be working?" I asked.
38 "Yes, but it's a **glorious** summer afternoon," Benvenuto said.
47 "I thought I'd rather come with you than sit in a dark workshop."
60 "Signor Agnolo will be angry," I said.
67 "No, he won't. I'll finish my work when I get back, and then
80 he won't have anything to complain about — if he even notices
91 I'm gone," he added, smiling mischievously.
97 I knew he was right. Benvenuto Cellini was by far the most
109 talented of the apprentices at Signor Agnolo's goldsmith shop.
118 He could finish any amount of work faster than anyone else. It would
131 be twice as good, too. Signor Agnolo knew that if he got rid of
145 Benvenuto, he would go to another shop. Then that goldsmith
155 would benefit from his talent.
160 My parents had sent me to Signor Agnolo's only three months ago,
172 right after my twelfth birthday. It was time for me to learn a trade. 186

Comprehension Check

1. What can you tell about Benvenuto's character? **Character**

2. What is Benvenuto trying to accomplish in his conversation with his friend? **Persuasion**

	Words Read	–	Number of Errors	=	Words Correct Score
First Read		–		=	
Second Read		–		=	

At Home: Help the student read the passage, paying attention to the goal at the top of the page.

Name ____________________

On the lines below, write a set of directions that describe how to make a simple drawing. It could be a drawing of an animal, a face, a house, or anything you can describe in a few simple steps. List the materials that will be needed to follow the directions. Be sure to number your steps.

At Home: Try to follow the directions the student wrote. If any steps are unclear, discuss how they could be rewritten for clarity.

Name ____________________

Write a description that could be used as a context clue for each of the following words. Then do the same for a word of your choice.

1. easel ____________________

2. kiln ____________________

3. portfolio ____________________

4. museum ____________________

5. sketches ____________________

At Home: Together, choose several unfamiliar words from an article in a newspaper or magazine. Look for context clues in the surrounding words to figure out the words' meanings.

Name ______________________________

Under each heading, write three words with the /ər/ sound that have the indicated spelling. Then use the words in a sentence.

1. /ər/ spelled *ar*

________ ________ ________

2. Sentence: ______________________________

____

____

3. /ər/ spelled *er*

________ ________ ________

4. Sentence: ______________________________

____

____

5. /ər/ spelled *or*

________ ________ ________

6. Sentence: ______________________________

____

____

At Home: Say the following word pairs and ask the student to name the word that does not have the /ər/ ending sound. (harbor, horn; popular, star; Ferris wheel, danger)

Name ______________________________

fragile	threatened	descendants
glistening	sanctuary	habitat
coaxing		

Using pencil, fill in the crossword puzzle with the vocabulary words above. Then write the clues below.

1
2 3
4
5
6
7

Erase the answers from the puzzle. Exchange pages with a partner and solve each other's puzzles.

Across

2. ______________________________

5. ______________________________

7. ______________________________

Down

1. ______________________________

3. ______________________________

4. ______________________________

6. ______________________________

Name ______________________

Every **cause** has an **effect**, and every effect has a cause.

For each cause given below, write a likely effect. For each effect given below, write a likely cause.

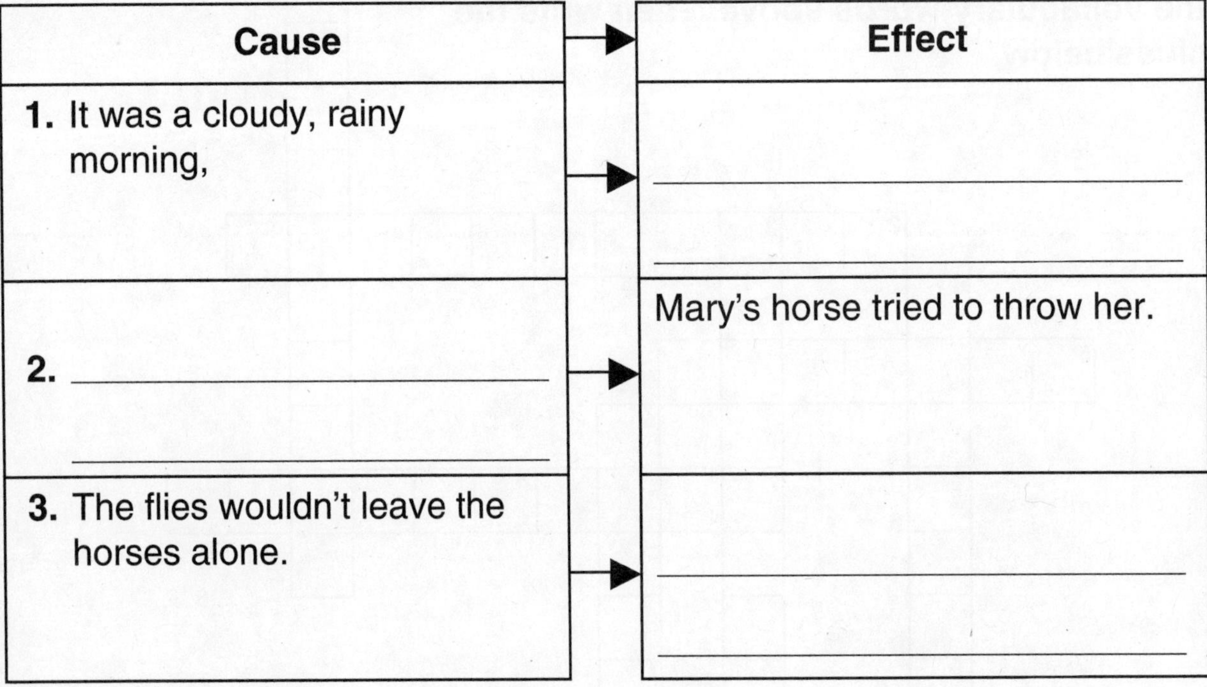

Cause		Effect
1. It was a cloudy, rainy morning,	→	______________________
2. ______________________	→	Mary's horse tried to throw her.
3. The flies wouldn't leave the horses alone.	→	______________________

4. Write your own sentences to show cause and effect.

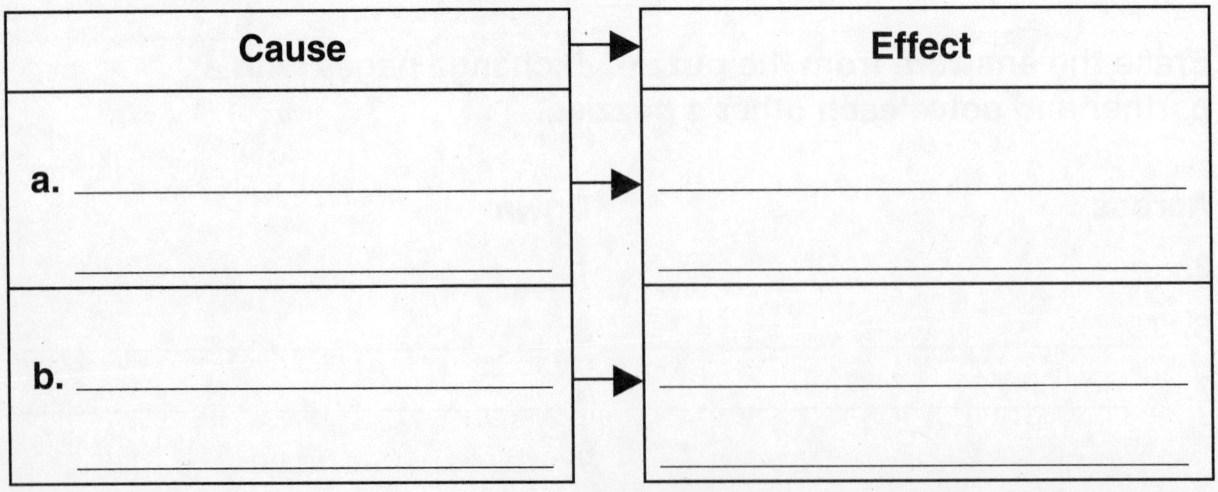

Cause		Effect
a. ______________________	→	______________________
b. ______________________	→	______________________

At Home: Read the following cause: *Because the electricity went out. . . .* Together, think of multiple effects that can be a result of the cause.

Name ____

As you read *Wild Horses,* fill in the Cause and Effect Diagram.

Cause	→	Effect
	→	
	→	
	→	
	→	

How does the information you wrote in the Cause and Effect Diagram help you to monitor your comprehension of *Wild Horses*?

At Home: Have the student use the chart to retell the story.

Name ____________________________________

As I read, I will pay attention to the pronunciation of vocabulary words.

Somewhere in Kentucky a thoroughbred horse has just been born.
10 Within hours the **glistening** newborn will be on its feet and taking its
23 first wobbly steps. The horse will stay close to its mother for about six
37 months. A horse breeder runs the farm. He has high hopes for this young
51 horse. Its mother and father were both fine racehorses.
60 When a young horse is ready to begin training, it is often sold to a new
76 owner. Some promising yearlings are sold for millions of dollars. The new
88 owner will make sure the horse receives the right training to become a
101 strong racehorse.
103 First a young racehorse must get used to wearing a bridle. Then the
116 horse must get used to carrying a rider on its back. Trainers teach these
130 new tasks gently and slowly. They don't want the horses to feel frightened
143 or **threatened**.
145 Young horses are not allowed to run fast until their bodies have grown.
158 In an exercise known as "ponying," a riderless horse is led around the track.
172 Trainers must also teach a horse to enter a starting gate. At first a horse
187 may be afraid of the starting gate. With gentle **coaxing**, the horse will
200 become used to it. 204

Comprehension Check

1. Why do trainers treat young racehorses so carefully? What do they hope the result will be? **Cause and Effect**

2. What kind of training do young racehorses receive? **Summarize**

	Words Read	–	Number of Errors	=	Words Correct Score
First Read		–		=	
Second Read		–		=	

At Home: Help the student read the passage, paying attention to the goal at the top of the page.

Name ______________________________________

A **figure of speech** is an expressive use of language that cannot be understood if each word is taken literally. One kind of figure of speech is **hyperbole.** This is when a writer uses exaggeration to make part of the story more dramatic or funny.

Underline the figure of speech in each sentence. Then rewrite the sentence without it.

1. Paul said that the new ranch hand always had a headache because his head kept banging up against the sky.

____

2. I knew that Paul was just pulling my leg.

____

3. Our new ranch hand, Joe, sure loved chocolate chip cookies, though, and he'd wash them down with a river of milk.

____

4. I loved those cookies, too. The sad thing was my eyes were always bigger than my stomach.

____

5. I was tickled pink when Joe said he'd teach me how to use a lasso.

____

6. When I missed that calf and it started chasing me, Joe laughed his head off.

____

At Home: Together, play a game in which you take turns using figures of speech to describe people you know.

Name ______________________________

lasso	foal	gallop	dam

On the lines below, create a short story about a horse. Use all four words in the box. Begin by looking up each word. Then write your story, including context clues that make their meanings clear. Circle the words from the box, and underline your context clues.

____

____

____

____

____

____

____

____

____

____

____

____

____

____

____

At Home: Together with the student, read his or her story. Discuss how the use of context clues helped make the words' meanings clear.

Name ______________________________

labor	people	anvil	royal	middle
elephant	civil	several	travel	telephone
animal	bugle	agile	snorkel	

Read each word in the box and listen for the /əl/ sound. If the word has the /əl/ sound, write it below the correct spelling. If it does not have the /əl/ sound, mark it with an *X*. When you finish, choose four of the words and write two sentences, including two of the words in each.

/əl/ spelled al

____

____

____

____

/əl/ spelled el

____

____

____

____

/əl/ spelled il

____

____

____

____

/əl/ spelled le

____

____

____

____

Sentences:

____

____

____

____

At Home: Together, think of more words with the /əl/ sound for each category above. Which spelling of the /əl/ sound seems to be the most common?

Name ___________________________

advanced	bumbling	selfish	glistening	glorious
exasperated	famished	threatened	fragile	peculiar
positive	commotion	valuable	descendants	cranky

A. Beside each of the words below, write its antonym from the box.

1. ordinary ____________
2. generous ____________
3. unbreakable ____________
4. pleasant ____________
5. patient ____________
6. careful ____________
7. full ____________
8. worthless ____________
9. negative ____________
10. safe ____________

B. Complete each series below with the remaining five words in the box.

11. beginning intermediate ____________
12. nice beautiful ____________
13. ancestors living relatives ____________
14. silence conversation ____________
15. dull polished ____________

Name ______________________________

Use the words in the box to complete the story.

snuffled	period	barbecue	collage	coaxing
speciality	vessels	skyscraper	documenting	strutting

I was researching Spanish galleons and other **16.** ______________ of that historical **17.** ______________ when Tomás Velázquez came into the library. He spotted me and came **18.** ______________ over.

"Hey, Will! I'm glad I ran into you!" Tomás said. "I wanted to invite your family to a **19.** ______________ in Chapultepec Park on Saturday to celebrate my father's new show in Soho."

Tomás's dad was a **20.** ______________ artist, whose **21.** ______________ was **22.** ________________ and other city scenes. Why would Tomás invite me? I wondered. He never so much as spoke to me before.

"There will be a live band and lots of great food, Will," Tomás started **23.** ______________ me. "Oh, and ask your dad to bring a photographer, too, for **24.** ________________ the event in *The Tribune.*"

So that's it, I thought. My dad's a reporter! I **25.** ______________ really loudly and faked a cough. "I'll try to make it, Tomás, but I feel a bad cold coming on," I told him.

Name ______________________________

annoyed	prospectors	outstretched	circular
glinted	reference	disappointment	

Pretend that you are in California during the Gold Rush. What kind of people do you meet? Have you had any luck finding gold?

On the lines below, write a portion of a letter to the folks back home describing your adventures. Be sure to use as many of the vocabulary words as possible.

____

____

____

____

____

____

____

____

____

____

____

____

____

____

____

Name ______________________________

One **cause** can have many **effects**. Each thing that happens can become a cause of another event.

Write a humorous paragraph that includes a chain of events caused by one of the following:

- You press a button that says "WARNING! DO NOT PRESS!"
- You get on the wrong stagecoach in 1849.

____
____
____
____
____
____
____
____
____
____
____
____
____
____
____
____

At Home: Imagine the chain of events that might result from a family member winning a large amount of money.

Practice

Comprehension: Cause and Effect

Name ______________________________

As you read *The Gold Rush Game,* fill in the Cause and Effect Diagram.

Cause →	Effect
→	
→	
→	
→	

How does the information you wrote in the Cause and Effect Diagram help you to analyze the story structure of *The Gold Rush Game*?

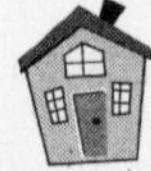

At Home: Have the student use the chart to retell the story.

Name ______________________________

As I read, I will pay attention to pauses, stops, and intonation.

If you want to know how a city is made, San Francisco is a good
15 place to learn.
18 The first residents of the area that became San Francisco were
29 Native Americans. For more than 10,000 years, the Ohlone nation lived
39 there. The land wasn't called San Francisco back then and there were
51 no buildings. The land was filled with trees, fields, and wild animals.
63 The Ohlone was not a single nation. It was actually a group of more
77 than 40 different bands. They lived in the same area, but had different
89 languages and customs. The name *Ohlone* actually means "western people."
99 The Ohlone did not live in a single place. They wandered the forests
112 and hills looking for food. If the land seemed good, they set up camp.
126 If not, they moved on.
131 There were usually many plants to eat and animals to hunt. The
143 Ohlone built small boats from wood and reeds. They had access to
154 many rivers, a giant bay, and the Pacific Ocean. There was not much
167 competition between the bands because there was so much food. They
178 shared the land and traded food and supplies. These natural riches
189 would eventually bring other wanderers and explorers. 196

Comprehension Check

1. Why was there little competition between the Ohlone bands? **Cause and Effect**

2. Was the San Francisco area a good place to live? Why? **Draw Conclusions**

	Words Read	–	Number of Errors	=	Words Correct Score
First Read		–		=	
Second Read		–		=	

At Home: Help the student read the passage, paying attention to the goal at the top of the page.

Name ______________________________

A. Read the timeline below. It describes events in the life of a fictional character during the time of the California Gold Rush.

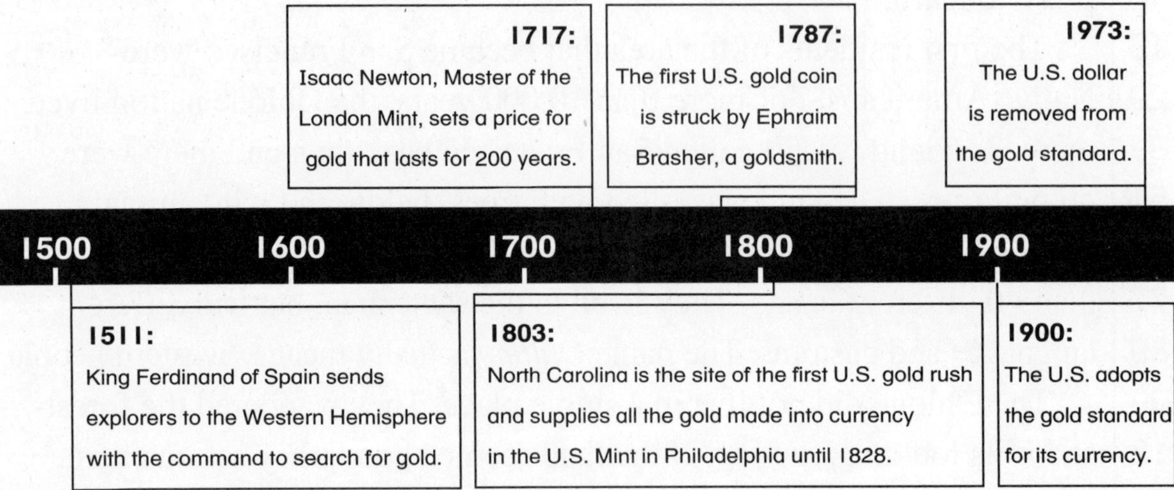

B. Use the timeline to answer the questions below.

1. Why are the points placed as they are? ______________________________

____

2. What might this timeline be named? ______________________________

____

3. How long was it from the time gold prices were set to the minting of the first coin in the United States? ______________

4. How long was it from the first gold coin to the decision to adopt the gold standard? ______________

5. How long ago was that decision made? ______________________________

____

6. Write your own question about the timeline. ______________________________

____

At Home: Together, create a timeline that tells about major events in your family's history.

Name ______________________________

Add the suffix *-er* or *-or* to the verbs in the box to create nouns. Write a sentence about the California Gold Rush using those nouns.

mine	travel	translate	instruct	act	settle	hike	visit

1. ______________________________

2. ______________________________

3. ______________________________

4. ______________________________

5. ______________________________

6. ______________________________

7. ______________________________

8. ______________________________

At Home: Take turns saying words with *-er* or *-or* endings until you run out of words.

Name ____________________

A. Answer each riddle with a word that ends in the final *ən* sound, spelled *-en, -in,* or *-on.*

1. I am the number of innings in a baseball game plus two.

What am I? ____________

2. I am a glass of water that was left outside on a 20° day.

What am I? ____________.

3. If you didn't have me, you wouldn't be able to stand straight.

What am I? ____________

4. I am a ship that is lying at the bottom of the sea.

What am I? ____________

5. I am the child of your mother's sister. Who am I? ____________

6. I grow where it is warm and I'm often used to make clothing.

What am I? ____________

7. I was a grape that was left in the sun to dry. Now I am wrinkled.

What am I? ____________

8. What does ice cream do when you leave it out for awhile?

____

B. Think of two more riddles yourself. Swap with a partner to solve.

9. ____________________

____

10. ____________________

____

At Home: Take turns making up riddles with answers that end in /ən/, spelled *-en, -in,* or *-on.*

Name ______________________________

eavesdropping	scuffling	wistfully	logical
jumble	scornfully	acquaintance	

Pretend that you are an animal on an adventure to a new and unfamiliar place. Write a letter to a friend back home describing your journey. Be sure to use each vocabulary word at least once.

Name ______________________________

Practice

Comprehension: Theme

The **theme** of a story is the story's overall main idea—what the story is about. The author may state it directly, or it may come across in what the characters say and do.
Examples of themes: friendship or facing new experiences

Write a story with animal characters that has one of the following themes. Show the theme in what happens or what characters say. Then trade your story with a partner, and discuss each other's themes.

- the comforts of home
- friends helping each other
- facing new experiences
- hidden strengths

____

____

____

____

____

____

____

____

____

____

____

At Home: Have the student read you his or her story and explain how it illustrates the chosen theme.

Name ______________________________

As you read *The Cricket in Times Square,* fill in the Theme Map.

Clue

↓

Clue

↓

Clue

↓

Clue

↓

Clue

↓

Theme

How does the information you wrote in the Theme Map help you to analyze the story structure of *The Cricket in Times Square*?

At Home: Have the student use the chart to retell the story.

Name ______________________________

As I read, I will pay attention to end punctuation in each sentence.

As Stella entered the little woods, a deer walked across the path. It
13 stopped to look at her. Stella had the odd feeling it was welcoming her.
27 In reply, she took out her lunch and put half of her apple on the path.
43 The deer took a dainty nibble of the apple and then finished it. It
57 looked at Stella with quiet brown eyes and then walked away through
69 the trees.

71 Stella kept walking. A few minutes later, she heard a **scuffling**
82 noise in the leaves. A squirrel popped its head out and looked at her
96 with bright eyes. Again Stella had the feeling it was welcoming her.
108 She smiled and offered the squirrel some walnuts from her lunch. The
120 squirrel packed the walnuts into its cheek, nodded its head
130 as if to say "thank you," and ran up the nearest tree.

142 Stella continued down the trail until she heard birds singing. Two
153 bluebirds swooped down. "Welcome," they seemed to sing.

161 Stella was puzzled. Why did it seem like all the animals were
173 greeting her? But she took out her sandwich and put some
184 breadcrumbs and a little piece of apple on a tree branch for the
197 bluebirds. They landed on the branch, ate the food, and flew away. 209

Comprehension Check

1. What are the themes of this passage? How do you know? **Theme**

2. How might Stella's generosity help her if she encounters trouble in the forest? **Draw Conclusions**

	Words Read	–	Number of Errors	=	Words Correct Score
First Read		–		=	
Second Read		–		=	

At Home: Help the student read the passage, paying attention to the goal at the top of the page.

Name ______________________________

Design an advertisement for a group, new product, or service. Use both words and illustration to make your product seem special in some way. Here are some ideas for products or services you might advertise:

- a new veterinary office that deals with wild animals
- an improved dog food
- a trip to Africa to photograph wild animals
- an organization that saves an endangered animal
- a whale-watching trip
- a fund-raiser for the local zoo

At Home: Together, identify techniques of persuasion in a TV or print advertisement.

Name ______________________________

Sometimes, you can figure out the meanings of unfamiliar words by looking for **context clues** in the same paragraph in which they are found.

Write a word or phrase that would work as a context clue for each of the words below. Then write a paragraph that includes the words and context clues.

Context Clues:

1. pulsate ______________________________

2. extinction ______________________________

3. consume ______________________________

4. safari ______________________________

____

____

____

____

____

____

____

____

____

____

At Home: Ask the student to read his or her paragraph and explain the context clues that he or she included.

Name ________________________________

deer/dear	sighed/side	heard/herd
peek/peak	rode/road	through/threw
wood/would	I/eye	fare/fair
knows/nose	knew/new	here/hear

Write a paragraph describing an encounter between a wild animal and a human being. Use as many of the homophone pairs listed above as you can.

____

____

____

____

____

____

____

____

____

____

____

____

____

____

____

At Home: Together, make up some sentences that include the homophone pairs above.

Name ______________________________

Imagine that you're on an archaeological dig on which your team has found something extraordinary and unexpected. Write a newspaper article about what your team has found and how they found it. Articles can be realistic or humorous. Use each vocabulary word at least once.

fossil	paleontologist	inspected	stumbled upon

Name ______________________________

A generalization can be true or not true. Read each generalization below. Based on what you have read and what you already know, decide whether it is true or not true and give reasons for your opinion.

1. Generalization: All paleontologists also dive for sunken ships.

   True or not true? ______________

   Why? ______________________________

   ____

   ____

2. Generalization: Most people who walk with their heads down will eventually find a dinosaur fossil.

   True or not true? ______________

   Why? ______________________________

   ____

   ____

3. Generalization: Paleontologists need to be adventurous, curious, and patient.

   True or not true? ______________

   Why? ______________________________

   ____

   ____

At Home: Together, think of three true generalizations that use the word *all.*

Name ______________________________

As you read *Meet a Bone-ified Explorer,* fill in the Generalizations Chart.

Information from Text	What I Know	Generalization

How does the information you wrote in this Generalizations Chart help you analyze the text structure of *Meet a Bone-ified Explorer*?

At Home: Have the student use the chart to retell the story.

Name ______________________________

As I read, I will pay attention to the pronunciation of vocabulary and other difficult words.

The auction was about to begin. For years, many people had waited
12 anxiously for this day. On October 4, 1997, in New York City, a
23 Tyrannosaurus rex named Sue came into the room and was put up for sale.
37 Well, really just her skull came into the room. Dinosaur Sue's skull
49 was 5 feet (1.5 m) long and weighed 600 pounds (272 kg). It looked
59 like a big boulder. But it was much more valuable than that.
71 Dinosaur Sue caused a lot of excitement when she was discovered by
83 **fossil** hunter Sue Hendrickson in 1990. Fossil hunters search for fossils.
93 Fossils are hardened remains of plants or animals that lived long ago.
105 Many fossil hunters search for dinosaur remains. The fossils of Dinosaur
116 Sue were carefully removed from their home in South Dakota, where
127 they had rested for 67 million years, and were put in storage.
138 Seven years later, Sue was sold and was finally ready to move to her new
153 home. The Field Museum in Chicago had shocked everyone by bidding
164 nearly $8.4 million for Sue at the auction.
171 Dinosaur Sue lived during a period of Earth's history called the
182 Mesozoic (mez-uh-ZOH-ik) Era. 184

Comprehension Check

1. Do museums usually buy fossils in auctions? How do you know? **Make Generalizations**

2. Why did Dinosaur Sue cause a lot of excitement? **Cause and Effect**

	Words Read	–	Number of Errors	=	Words Correct Score
First Read		–		=	
Second Read		–		=	

At Home: Help the student read the passage, paying attention to the goal at the top of the page.

Name ______________________________

An **application** is a **functional document** that provides the information needed for someone to decide whether the applicant is suitable. An application may be for the purpose of entering a program, receiving an award or grant, being hired, or for a variety of other reasons.

Practice filling out an application by filling out the one below.

Dinosaur Camp Application Form

Camper's Name ______________________________

Address: ____________ City: ____________

State: ______ Zip Code: ______ Home Phone: ____________

Age: ______ Birthday: ______ 2007/2008 Grade Level: ______

School: ______________________________

Session(s) I Wish to Attend: July 12–16 ___ July 19–23 ___

July 26–30 ___ Aug. 9–13 ___

Have you attended dinosaur camp previously? ___ If so, when? ______

Why do you want to go to Dinosaur Camp? ______________________________

____

I hereby give my permission for ____________________ to attend Dinosaur Camp.

__________ ______________________________

Date Signature of Parent or Guardian

At Home: Together, discuss the purpose of functional documents, such as advertisements, forms, and circulars, that are mailed to your home.

Name ____

Words that include the Latin root *aud-* have something to do with sound or hearing.
Words that include the Latin root *spec-* have something to do with sight or seeing.

Make up a sentence that includes each of the words shown.

1. auditorium ____

____

2. spectrum ____

____

3. inspection ____

____

4. audition ____

____

5. spectacle ____

____

6. auditory ____

____

At Home: Have the student read the sentences and explain how context would help someone understand what each word means.

Name ______________________________

Write as many words as you can that begin with the prefixes *dis-, non-, un-,* and *mis-*.

dis-

____
____
____
____
____
____
____
____

un-

____
____
____
____
____
____
____
____

non-

____
____
____
____
____
____
____
____

mis-

____
____
____
____
____
____
____
____

At Home: Together, see if you can come up with any more words with the prefixes *dis-*, *non-*, *un-*, and *mis-*.

Name ______________________________

Answer the questions using a vocabulary word in each answer.

glider	unstable	wingspan	applauded
headlines	hoisting	assured	

1. How is a glider different from a passenger jet?

____

____

2 Compare the wingspan of a hummingbird to that of a condor.

____

____

3. For what event has the audience applauded the longest?

____

____

4. What item might need hoisting by a crane?

____

____

5. Explain why a bicycle is more unstable than a tricycle.

____

____

Name ______________________________

Read the passage. Then respond to it in two paragraphs. Start by explaining the author's perspective. Then explain your own perspective.

Should there be a minimum age limit for people who want to take flying lessons? In the past, people of any age could learn to fly. Several years ago, three people died trying to break the world record for the youngest pilot. One of them was seven years old.

It is good for young people to try out new things. But when it leads to taking huge risks, it should not be encouraged.

The author's perspective:

____

____

____

____

____

____

My perspective:

____

____

____

____

____

____

At Home: Have the student read to you what he or she wrote on this page and explain his or her perspective.

Name ____

As you read *My Brother's Flying Machine,* fill in the Author's Perspective Map.

Clue	Clue	Clue

↓ ↓ ↓

Author's Perspective

How does the information you wrote in the Author's Perspective Map help you to monitor your comprehension of *My Brothers' Flying Machine*?

At Home: Have the student use the chart to retell the story.

Name ______________________________

As I read, I will pay attention to tempo in order to match the action in the story.

Bessie Coleman was the first African American woman to fly a
11 plane. She built a career as a famous barnstormer, a pilot who does
24 tricks in an airplane.
28 Bessie was born on January 26, 1892. Her family soon moved to
38 Waxahachie, Texas. Bessie grew up in a segregated society. Black and
49 white children lived in different neighborhoods and went to separate
59 schools. It was not an easy life.
66 Bessie's family was poor. Her mother worked to support them.
76 Bessie helped take care of her younger sister. She always knew that
88 she wanted to make something of herself. And she did. Bessie worked
100 hard, finished high school, and left home for a college education.
111 At that time flying was a new and exciting adventure. Bessie read
123 about the Wright Brothers and their historic flight at Kitty Hawk in
135 1903. She also read about a woman pilot named Harriet Quimby.
146 Bessie was surprised to learn that women flew, and she started to think
159 about flying herself.
162 In 1915 Bessie moved to Chicago to live near her older brother.
173 She found work and set out to learn to fly. 183

Comprehension Check

1. What obstacles did Bessie Coleman overcome to be a pilot? **Summarize**

2. What opinion did Bessie have about pilots? How did Harriet Quimby change Bessie's mind? **Fact and Opinion**

	Words Read	–	Number of Errors	=	Words Correct Score
First Read		–		=	
Second Read		–		=	

At Home: Help the student read the passage, paying attention to the goal at the top of the page.

Name ______________________________

Practice

Literary Elements: Repetition and Personification

Repetition: using a sound, word, or phrase two or more times for emphasis.
Personification: giving animals or things human characteristics.

A. Write a short poem or a couple of sentences about an exciting event, using repetition at least once.

____

____

____

____

B. Write a short poem about a common household appliance, such as a vacuum cleaner or dishwasher. Use personification to make the poem more interesting.

____

____

____

____

____

____

____

____

____

____

At Home: Have the student read his or her work to you and tell where he or she used personification and repetition.

Name ______________________________

When a verb ends in a consonant *-e*, drop the *e* before adding *-ed*.
chase + ed = chased
When a verb ends in a consonant and *y*, change the *y* to *i* before adding *-ed*.
spy + ed = spied
When a verb ends in a consonant preceded by a single vowel, double the consonant before adding *-ed*.
control + ed = controlled

Add the inflected ending *-ed* to the following words.

1. compose ________________

2. realize ________________

3. create ________________

4. aviate ________________

5. happen ________________

6. carry ________________

7. cry ________________

8. permit ________________

9. squirm ________________

10. marry ________________

11. weigh ________________

12. trade ________________

13. shop ________________

14. question ________________

At Home: Take turns using two of the words with *-ed* in a sentence.

Name ______________________________

Adding suffixes to the end of words changes their meanings.

sorrow + *ful* = full of sorrow

might + *y* = full of might

sincere + *ly* = in a sincere way

silly + *ness* = the state of being silly

sense + *less* = without sense

Add the correct suffix to the base word given. Then use the word you made in a sentence.

1. without power ______________

____

2. full of beauty ______________

____

3. in a careful way ______________

____

4. full of snow ______________

____

5. the state of being happy ______________

____

6. in a proud way ______________

____

At Home: Have the student read you his or her sentences and point out the words with suffixes.

Name ______________________________

A. Write a definition in your own words for each vocabulary word.

1. astronomer ______________________________
____

2. communication ______________________________
____

3. investigates ______________________________
____

4. nutrients ______________________________
____

B. Write a sentence using each vocabulary word. Use each word in a context that shows its meaning.

5. solitary ______________________________
____

6. prehistoric ______________________________
____

7. territory ______________________________
____

8. overcome ______________________________
____

Name ______________________________

Describe life in an ant colony from an ant's point of view. Write one or more sentences with sensory details for each of the five senses; sight, hearing, smell, touch, and taste.

Sight: ______________________________

____

____

Hearing: ______________________________

____

____

Smell: ______________________________

____

____

Touch: ______________________________

____

____

Taste: ______________________________

____

____

At Home: Ask the student to read you his or her description and to point out the sensory details he or she included.

Name ______________________________

Practice

Comprehension: Description Web

As you read *The Life and Times of the Ant,* fill in the Description Web.

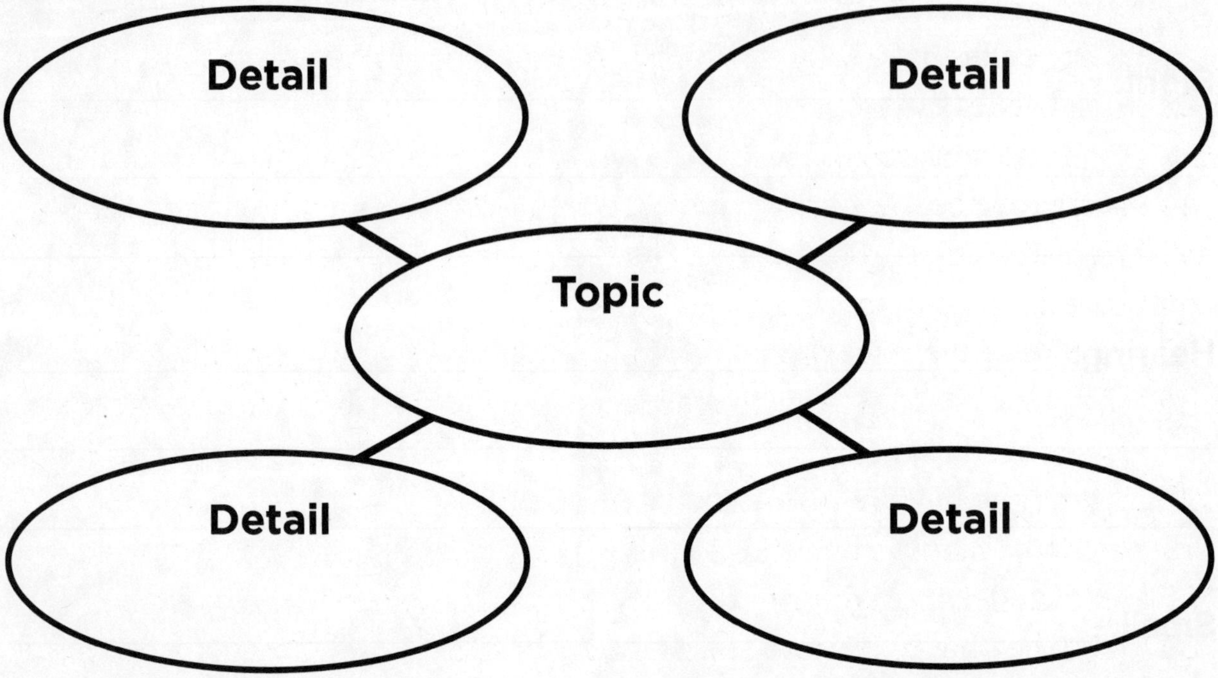

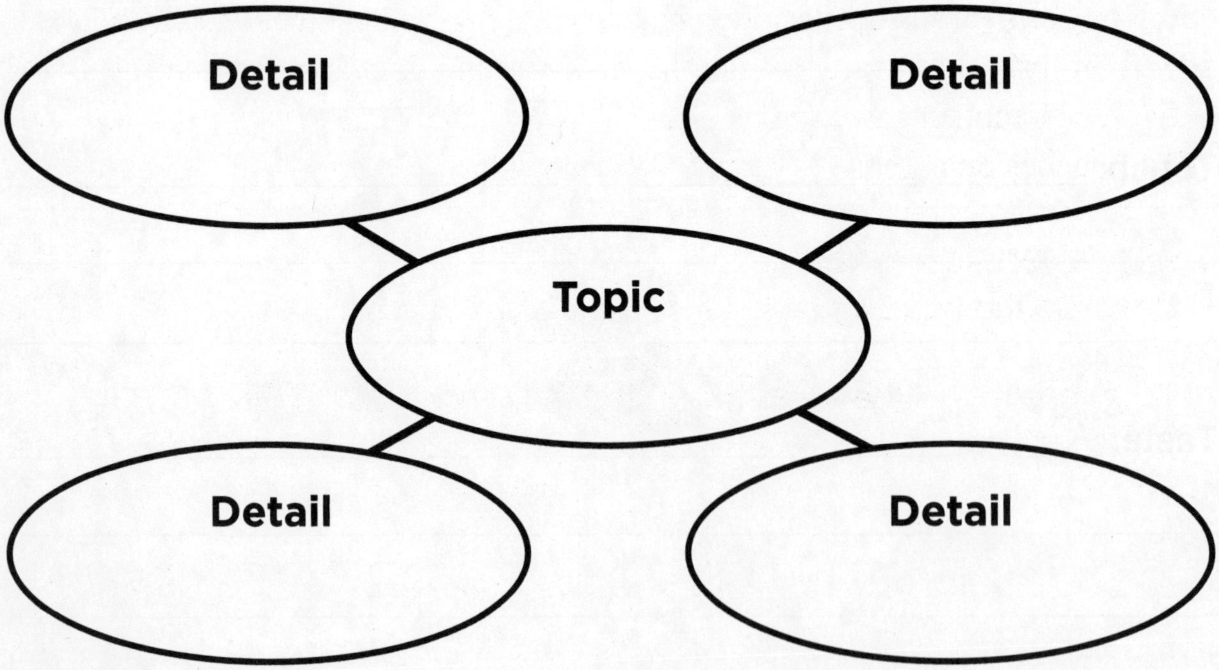

Detail

Detail

Topic

Detail

Detail

Detail

Detail

Topic

Detail

Detail

How does completing the Description Web help you analyze the text structure of *The Life and Times of the Ant*?

At Home: Have the student use the chart to retell the story.

Name ______________________________

As I read, I will pay attention to the pronunciation of vocabulary words.

Some beetles are **solitary**. They aggressively defend their **territory**.
9 Stag beetles have long mandibles, or jaws, which they use to move other
22 stag beetles out of the way.
28 There are beetles who make their homes with other insects. For example,
40 some rove beetles move in with ant or termite communities. The beetle
52 gets protection from the insect colony. In return, it keeps the colony clean
65 by eating the other animals' waste products.
72 One of the reasons that beetles have survived so successfully is that
84 they have adapted to eat the foods that are found in different environments.
97 Some beetle species are herbivores, or plant eaters. Other beetle species
108 are carnivores, predators that eat other animals.
115 Some herbivore beetles eat only living plants and leaves. Other beetles
126 feed on dead and rotting wood and plants. These beetles do an important
139 job. They break down the plant materials so the **nutrients** can be recycled
152 back into the soil.
156 Carnivorous beetles often have strong jaws to help them catch and eat
168 their prey. For example, tiger beetle larvae build long vertical burrows.
179 When another insect comes close, the larva darts out of its burrow,
191 pounces on its prey, and drags it home to eat. 201

Comprehension Check

1. Describe the burrow of a tiger beetle larva. **Description**

2. Do all beetles act the same way in order to survive? Why? **Draw Conclusions**

	Words Read	–	Number of Errors	=	Words Correct Score
First Read		–		=	
Second Read		–		=	

At Home: Help the student read the passage, paying attention to the goal at the top of the page.

Name ______________________________

A. Write a fable. First, choose a moral. Circle one of the choices below, or write your own moral in the space provided.

One good turn deserves another.

Friendship is more important than wealth.

Hard work is rewarded.

Obey your elders.

Treat others as you want to be treated.

Other: ______________

B. Now think about the characters and plot of the fable. Note the main events and the characters that experience them on the lines below. Be sure that the plot helps readers understand your moral.

____

____

____

C. Use your plot summary to write your fable. Write the moral as the final line of the story.

____

____

____

____

____

____

____

____

At Home: Have the student read his or her fable to you. Discuss the moral.

Name ______________________________

A **root word** is a word part used to build longer words. For example, the word *helicopter* contains the Greek root word *helic*, meaning "spiral" and the root word *pteron*, meaning "wing." A helicopter is an aircraft whose wings move in a spiral motion.

Root Word	Meaning	Root Word	Meaning
bio-	life	-logy	the study of
geo-	Earth	-graph	write
tele-	distant	-scope	see
dino-	monster	-saur	lizard

A. Use the Root Word Chart above to write a meaning of each word below.

1. geology ______________________

2. biography ______________________

3. dinosaur ______________________

4. biology ______________________

B. Use the clues below to write a word. Then write a definition for each word.

5. tele + photo ("light") = ________________

____

6. tele + graph = ________________

____

7. astro ("star") + naut ("sailor") = ________________

____

8. tele + scope ("see") = ________________

____

At Home: With the student, try to come up with more words that use the Greek roots on this page.

Name ______________________________

List as many words with the /ûr/ sound as you can below each spelling. Draw a line under the accented syllable in each word. Then write three sentences, each using at least one word for each spelling.

/ûr/ spelled *er*	/ûr/ spelled *ir*	/ûr/ spelled *ur*
____________	____________	____________
____________	____________	____________
____________	____________	____________
____________	____________	____________
____________	____________	____________

1. ____

____

2. ____

____

3. ____

____

At Home: Have the student ask you riddles with one-word answers that have the /*er*/ sound.

Name ______________________________

A. Find the words in the box that are synonyms for the words given and write them on the lines.

reference	nutrients	investigates	wistfully
annoyed	eavesdropping	prospectors	glinted
fossil	disappointment	astronomer	territory
applauded	stumbled upon	unstable	hoisting
inspected	scornfully	assured	circular
overcome	communication	jumble	logical

1. irritated ______________________

2. pensively ______________________

3. letdown ______________________

4. sparkled ______________________

5. round ______________________

6. snooping ______________________

7. guaranteed ______________________

8. hodgepodge ______________________

9. miners ______________________

10. nutritious substances ______________________

11. to rise above ______________________

12. a person or thing that is referred to ______________________

13. rational ______________________

14. wobbly ______________________

15. mockingly ______________________

16. examined ______________________

17. came across ______________________

18. lifting ______________________

19. clapped ______________________

20. researches ______________________

21. land ______________________

22. ancient remains ______________________

23. message ______________________

24. expert dealing with planets and stars ______________________

Name ____________________

outstretched	acquaintance	solitary
paleontologist	headlines	glider
prehistoric	wingspan	scuffling

B. Complete the passage with words from the box above.

Magdalena Murphy took the ______________ hand offered to her and said, "It's certainly a pleasure to make your ______________, Dr. Haversham. How long have you been working here at the Museum of Natural History?"

"About twelve years now, I think. And during this time so many discoveries have come to light. But, of course, you know this. As a science reporter, many of those ______________ were on articles you wrote yourself, Ms. Murphy."

"That's true, Dr. Haversham. I must say I enjoy writing about ______________ specimens the most. I guess if I didn't get my degree in journalism, I might have become a ______________ such as yourself. Now, Dr. Haversham, I've been wanting to ask you this question for some time: If you could choose a single, ______________ dinosaur as a favorite, which one would you pick?"

"That's quite a difficult decision. Hmmm. I guess I'm most intrigued by the flying dinosaurs, so my favorite would be the pteranodon, with its forty-foot ______________. The wings of a modern ______________ can reach fifty feet, so you can get some idea of how impressive pteranodons must have been in flight."